Music of the Bach Family

KARL GEIRINGER

Music of the Bach Family

ᴀN ANTHOLOGY

HARVARD UNIVERSITY PRESS   CAMBRIDGE   1955

DISTRIBUTED IN GREAT BRITAIN BY GEOFFREY CUMBERLEGE,
OXFORD UNIVERSITY PRESS, LONDON

LIBRARY OF CONGRESS CATALOG CARD NUMBER M55–1017
PRINTED IN THE UNITED STATES OF AMERICA

Preface

During the seventeenth and eighteenth centuries, when it was customary for a son to take over the position of his father, families of musicians were no rare occurrence. The Couperins in France, the Ahles and the Lindemanns in Germany were among these famous musical dynasties. No other artistic family, however, equals in distinction the Bachs, who both in quantity and quality of achievement tower above all others.

The history of the Bach musicians starts at the beginning of the seventeenth century with a music-loving miller, Veit Bach, whose son Johannes worked as *Spielmann* in the German province of Thuringia. Henceforth organists and town pipers by the name of Bach appeared in large numbers, some of them having remarkable artistic stature. The third generation after Johannes witnessed the dynasty's most splendid flowering in the person of Johann Sebastian. Even the appearance of this genius did not exhaust the Bachs' artistic power. Musical talent miraculously flourished in Sebastian's sons, who were able to exercise a decisive influence on the music of their times.

In this anthology twenty-seven compositions by fourteen different Bachs are offered. The earliest of these works originated around the middle of the seventeenth century, the latest near 1800. Practically every type of music is represented: compositions for organ and clavier, the motet, the sacred and the secular cantata, chamber music, and — as far as is possible within the limited scope of such a publication — the symphony and music for the stage. The editor's aim is not only to illustrate the unique significance of this family of musicians, which produced a seemingly unending stream of highly gifted artists, but also to provide a selection of interesting compositions, largely unavailable in other editions, which illuminate various phases of stylistic development from the baroque to the classical eras. About two thirds of the music in this volume is presented for the first time in a modern edition, including most of the works by contemporaries and descendants of Johann Sebastian Bach, such as Johann Bernhard, Johann Ludwig, Wilhelm Friedemann, Carl Philipp Emanuel, Johann Ernst, and Johann Christian.

Compositions by the greatest of all the Bachs are not included in this selection. J. Sebastian's work is too firmly rooted in our musical consciousness to justify the attempt to represent his art with the help of only a few specimens. However, the student of this anthology will again and again find in the works of other Bachs features familiar to him from Sebastian's music. The Cantor of St. Thomas learned a great deal from his kinsmen, and he diligently copied many of their works. It is significant that some of the compositions by other Bach musicians —

PREFACE

one of them reprinted here — have for a long time been attributed to Sebastian. On the other hand a master of such eminence could not but leave his impress on the Bachs who followed him, eager though they were to achieve artistic independence; and thus Johann Sebastian, though not represented in this anthology, still stands at its very center.

While it has been the editor's aim to reproduce faithfully the original sources (merely rectifying indisputable errors in the manuscripts and modernizing the clefs), in some instances he obviously had to present excerpts and compress the scores. As a rule the realization of the thorough bass has been provided so as to facilitate performance. In the case of vocal works the original text is reproduced with the music, and an English translation added in the prefatory notes.

The histories of the individual Bachs can only be outlined in our brief introductory commentaries. It is the editor's hope that the examples presented will kindle interest in a unique dynasty of musicians. For this reason bibliographical information and a selected list of current editions * were supplied for each composer. After careful deliberation it was decided, in view of the fluctuating situation in this field, not to include lists of gramophone records. Readers interested in recordings of works by members of the Bach family should consult, in addition to current catalogs, Francis T. Clough and G. J. Cuming, *The World's Encyclopedia of Recorded Music*, London, 1952, and its supplements.

The editor is well aware that, in spite of all the care taken, errors may have occurred. He would be grateful if readers informed him of any mistakes they find.

It is the editor's pleasant duty to express his sincere gratitude to the American Philosophical Society of Philadelphia and to Jerome Hill, Esq., who helped make his research possible. Cordial thanks for unfailing assistance are also due to the directors of the Westdeutsche Bibliothek, Marburg; the Universitätsbibliothek, Tübingen; the Deutsche Staatsbibliothek, Berlin; the Gesellschaft der Musikfreunde, Vienna; the British Museum, London; the Bibliothèque du Conservatoire, Brussels; the Library of Congress, Washington, D.C.; and to Professor George B. Weston, Cambridge, whose scores used for this anthology have since become the property of Harvard University. For valuable assistance the editor is indebted to former and present members of his Collegium Musicum at Boston University, especially to his friend and colleague, Dr. Artin Arslanian, to Dr. Max Miller, and to Dr. Manus Sasonkin. Dr. Henry S. Drinker very kindly provided English translations for some of the German texts, and Dr. Camillo Merlino helped with a translation from the Italian.

KARL GEIRINGER

Boston, June 1955

* The titles of the compositions are usually condensed to save space. The name of the editor and the year of publication were added when they were available.

Contents

List of Abbreviations

Lower case letters indicate a minor key, capitals a major key (a = A minor, A = A major)

BG —	Collected Edition of J. S. Bach's works edited by Bach Gesellschaft. Leipzig, 1851–1900.
B & H —	Breitkopf & Härtel, Leipzig.
BJ —	*Bach Jahrbuch.* Leipzig, 1904–1950.
BV —	Bärenreiter Verlag. Kassel.
DDT —	*Denkmäler deutscher Tonkunst.* Leipzig, 1892–1931.
FP —	First printing. This designation is used under the heading "Source" for compositions which, to the knowledge of the editor, have not been made available before in any modern edition.
K. Geiringer —	*The Bach Family: Seven Generations of Creative Genius* by Karl Geiringer in collaboration with Irene Geiringer. New York, 1954.
Grove —	*Grove's Dictionary of Music and Musicians,* fifth edition, edited by Eric Blom, vol. I. London, 1954.
MGG —	*Die Musik in Geschichte und Gegenwart,* edited by Friedrich Blume, vol. I. Kassel, 1949–1951.
NMA —	*Nagels Musikarchiv,* Hannover.
RD —	*Das Erbe deutscher Musik. Reichsdenkmale,* 1935– .
P. Spitta —	*J. S. Bach* by Philip Spitta, translated by Clara Bell and J. A. Fuller Maitland. London, 1884–1885, reprinted 1951.

Music of the Bach Family

MUSICIANS OF THE BACH FAMILY

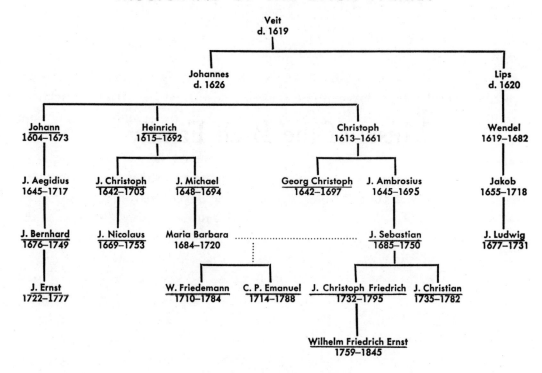

Veit
d. 1619

Johannes
d. 1626

Lips
d. 1620

Johann
1604–1673

Heinrich
1615–1692

Christoph
1613–1661

Wendel
1619–1682

J. Aegidius
1645–1717

J. Christoph
1642–1703

J. Michael
1648–1694

Georg Christoph
1642–1697

J. Ambrosius
1645–1695

Jakob
1655–1718

J. Bernhard
1676–1749

J. Nicolaus
1669–1753

Maria Barbara
1684–1720

J. Sebastian
1685–1750

J. Ludwig
1677–1731

J. Ernst
1722–1777

W. Friedemann
1710–1784

C. P. Emanuel
1714–1788

J. Christoph Friedrich
1732–1795

J. Christian
1735–1782

Wilhelm Friedrich Ernst
1759–1845

Johann Bach (1604–1673)

JOHANN, a son of Johannes, is the oldest member of the family to be represented in a collection of Bach compositions started by Johann Ambrosius, father of Sebastian, and continued by the Thomas Cantor himself. The fact that Ambrosius and Sebastian devoted much effort and time to the establishment of the so-called "Alt-Bachisches Archiv" reveals the pride they felt in the creative work of their forebears. It is fortunate that this significant collection, which disappeared during the nineteenth century, was gradually reassembled in our time and is now preserved in the library of the Singakademie, Berlin.

Johann occupied a central place among the members of the clan. He secured in 1635 a position as town musician in the city of Erfurt and subsequently was also organist to its Predigerkirche. Although he never achieved the rank of director of the town band (as Spitta and other scholars have assumed), he wielded great influence. Several of his relatives received musical employment at Erfurt through his good offices, and their work must have proved wholly satisfactory, since Bach musicians served in the town without a break up to the year 1813.

In Johann's home, which was as modest as it was hospitable, many Bachs were given thorough musical training. Here Johann's two gifted brothers, Heinrich and Christoph, lived while working in the Erfurt band, until they found better positions in another town; and they were followed by numerous members of the younger generation, among them Sebastian's father.

Johann's second wife, Hedwig, had the maiden name of Lämmerhirt and thus belonged to a family which has achieved immortality through Elisabeth Lämmerhirt, the mother of Sebastian. Consequently Johann's descendants (some of them distinguished composers represented in our anthology) were related to Sebastian on two sides, through the mother as well as through the father.

Only three of Johann's compositions are known to us. They were preserved in the "Alt-Bachisches Archiv" and consist of two motets, for a long time erroneously ascribed to Johann's nephew, Johann Michael, and a hymn-like "aria." The compositions reveal an austere monumentality which seems to grow out of the personal experiences of the composer, whose life was spent to a large extent under the shadow of the Thirty Years' War and its local sequels. He writes simple homo-

JOHANN BACH (1604-1673)

phonic music in which, according to the custom of the time, words from the Bible are combined with those from Protestant chorales.

Probably the most significant of his works is the chorale motet "Unser Leben ist ein Schatten," a substantial section of which is included in our anthology. The motet is written for a six-part chorus of two sopranos, one alto, two tenors, and one bass, and a "chorus latens" (hidden chorus) consisting of alto, tenor, and bass only. This second vocal group, which is mainly entrusted with the singing of the chorales, was probably meant to be located at a distance from the other musicians; and as it alternates with the main chorus, a most impressive coloristic contrast is achieved. In the beginning of the motet, when the futility of earthly matters is emphasized, the composer uses eerie tonal figures to conjure the picture of fast-moving shadows. In this gloomy atmosphere a ray of light appears when the distant chorus intones two stanzas of a chorale promising to frail human beings the support and consolation of mankind's salvation through Jesus. The end of the motet reverts to the dark mood of the beginning. After the chorus has ceased to present its desperate statement that everybody — old, young, rich, wise, lovely — must depart, the two sopranos remain, dejectedly repeating the last word. Nothing could depict human evanescence more poignantly than these two isolated voices which seem to float to us out of complete emptiness.

It is interesting to note that Johann's grandnephew Sebastian used a similar effect in his early funeral cantata (No. 106), "Gottes Zeit." At the end of the chorus "Es ist der alte Bund," altos, tenors, basses, and eventually the instruments fade away, and the sopranos alone call out for the Saviour. The mood is, however, a different one; the despair of the earlier work is transformed here into fervent hope.

The text of Johann's motet reads in a free English translation:

Our existence is a shadow on earth here.

Well I know that life is fleeting
Like a cloudy misty breath,
Ever near there hovers death.
One day soon we shall be meeting,
Tho' it may not be today;
By my side will Jesus stay.

If perchance it be tomorrow,
That I bid farewell to life,
Mortal care and mortal strife;
Joy will drive away all sorrow.
Darkness will be brightest day.
By my side will Jesus stay.

JOHANN BACH (1604–1673)

Ah teach us, Lord, to bear in mind
That we are mortal human kind.
Our day to die is ever nigh.
Ev'ry mortal must surely die.
The wise, rich, young, or lovely,
Ev'ry mortal must surely die.

SOURCE OF COMPOSITION REPRODUCED HERE: (Schneider) *RD*, vol. I, p. 9.

BIBLIOGRAPHY

R. Benecke in *MGG*, p. 905.
K. Geiringer, pp. 13–18, 25–28.
H. Lämmerhirt, "Bachs Mutter und ihre Sippe," *BJ*, 1925.
O. Rollert, "Die Erfurter Bache" in *Johann Sebastian Bach in Thüringen*. Weimar, 1950.
C. S. Terry in *Grove*, p. 287.
M. Schneider in *RD*, vol. I, p. v.
P. Spitta, vol. I, pp. 14–21, 70–73.

CURRENT EDITIONS OF OTHER WORKS

"Sei nun wieder zufrieden," motet (Schneider), *RD*, vol. I, p. 3.
"Weint nicht um meinen Tod," aria (Schneider), *RD*, vol. I, p. 18.

Johann Bach (1604–1673)

Unser Leben ist ein Schatten

Motet

6

Schat - - - - - ten, ein Schatten, ein Schat - - ten auf Er -

Schatten, ein Schatten, ein Schat - - ten auf Er -

Schatten, ein Schatten ein Schatten, ein Schatten, ein Schatten auf Er -

Chorus II. (latens)

den, un-ser Leben ist ein Schatten auf Er - den.

den, un-ser Leben ist ein Schat - ten auf Er - den. 1. Ich weiss wohl, dass un-ser Le-ben

den, un-ser Leben ist ein Schatten auf Er - den. 2. Sterb'ich bald, so komm ich a - be

7

Chorus I. Chorus II.

1. zu je der Frist

1. oft nur als ein Ne bel ist, denn wir hier zu je der Frist 1. zu jeder Frist mit dem To de

2. von der Welt Be schwer lich keit, ru he bis zur vol len Freud 2. Zur vol len Freud und weiss, dass im

Chorus I.

meinen Je sum

seind um ge ben drum ob's heu te nicht ge schicht meinen Je sum lass ich nicht, meinen Je sum

fin stern Gra be Je sus ist mein hel les Licht, meinen Je sum lass ich nicht, meinen Je sum

von,

da - von, da - von, müs - sen al - le da - von, ge - lehrt, reich,

al - le, al - le, al - le müs - sen al - le, al - le, al - le da - von, müs - sen al - le da - von,

al - le, al - le, al - le da - von, da - von, da - von, müs - sen al - le da - von,

jung, reich, jung o - der schön, müs - sen al - le, al - le, al - le da - von, da - von.

ge - lehrt, alt o - der schön, müs - sen al - le, al - le, al - le da - von, da - von.

ge - lehrt, alt o - der schön, müs - sen al - le, al - le, al - le da - von, da - von.

Heinrich Bach (1615–1692)

HEINRICH, Johann's younger brother, was mainly interested in the organ, and it is reported that as a child he walked miles and miles to reach a village boasting a good instrument. He served as an outstanding organist from 1641 until his death in the Thuringian town of Arnstadt, where his friendliness, his gentle humor, and his deep religiousness made him generally beloved. Heinrich's life was anything but easy. The small court of the Counts of Schwarzburg-Arnstadt, where he was employed, suffered great damage through the Thirty Years' War, and only too often the organist had to manage for long periods without a salary. Heinrich bore this bravely, not losing a cheerful outlook on life; and with what looks like miraculous skill to us he succeeded in raising five children, three of whom were eminent musicians.

His reputation was based not only on his feats at the organ but on his creative work as well, and it spread beyond the confines of Thuringia. When his grandnephew Sebastian traveled 200 miles northward to the town of Lüneburg, he found in its St. Michael's Church a composition by Heinrich Bach. Similarly the funeral sermon on the artist, delivered by J. G. Olearius and handed down in print, mentions chorales, motets, concertos, preludes, and fugues he composed. Of this huge output only a single work has been preserved. Two more are known to us by name, while in several other cases Heinrich's authorship, which used to be assumed, can no longer be upheld. The lament "Ach dass ich Wassers g'nug hätte," once attributed to Heinrich, is the work of his son Johann Christoph; while two chorale preludes bearing the initials "J. H. B." were probably written by the Thuringian composer Johann Heinrich Buttstädt. The aria for four voices, "Nun ist alles überwunden," preserved in the "Alt-Bachisches Archiv" and bearing the inscription "Arnstadt, 6 July 1686" but no author's name, was tentatively assigned by Schneider to Heinrich Bach; it seems unlikely, however, that the aged composer, who was seriously ailing during the last years of his life, could have written so powerful a composition.

The only piece irrefutably known to be a composition by Heinrich is the cantata "Ich danke dir, Gott," the greater part of which is reproduced in our anthology. The work, which was meant for the Seventeenth Sunday after Trinity and is

HEINRICH BACH (1615–1692)

dated 29 January, 1681, employs two violins, an alto and a tenor viola, and basso continuo. These instruments compete with a five-part vocal group of solo singers, the *favoriti*, reinforced when the occasion demands it by a larger five-part chorus, the *capella*. A significant role is allotted to the instruments, and the introductory *sinfonia* displays a gay competition between violins and violas. Such features of the baroque *stile concertato* are apparent throughout the composition, which abounds in cheerful rivalries between the different sound groups. This work with its sparkling coloraturas is as much a personal document as Johann Bach's somber motet. It is an ode of thanks to the Creator by a composer who, in spite of all the tribulations he suffered, found God's earth a good place to live in.

The text of Heinrich's cantata as reproduced here reads in free English translation:

> I thank Thee, God,
> For the wonder of Thy creation.
> Wonderful are Thy works,
> Of this my soul is well aware.

SOURCE OF COMPOSITION REPRODUCED HERE: (Schneider) *RD*, vol. II, p. 3.

BIBLIOGRAPHY

R. Benecke in *MGG*, p. 906.
K. Geiringer, pp. 20–23, 28–29.
J. G. Olearius, "Begräbnispredigt auf Heinrich Bach" in *Monatshefte für Musikgeschichte,* 1875.
M. Schneider in *RD*, vol. I, pp. v, vi.
P. Spitta, vol. I, pp. 27–37.
F. Wiegand, "Die Arnstädter Bache" in *J. S. Bach und seine Verwandten in Arnstadt*. Arnstadt, 1950.

Heinrich Bach (1615–1692)

Ich danke dir, Gott

Cantata

Ich, ich dan-ke dir, dan-ke dir, Gott, ich, ich dan-ke, dan-

bar-lich ge-macht bin,   dass ich wun . . . . der, wun . . . . der, wun . der . bar . lich gemacht bin.

dass ich wun . . . . der,-

. . .der, dass ich wun . . . . der . bar . lich gemacht bin,

dass ich wun . . . . der . bar . lich bin.

wun . . . der . bar . lich, wun . der . bar . lich gemacht bin.

dass ich wun . . . . der,-wun . . . . der,-wun . . . der . bar . lich gemacht bin.

6   4   3   6   7   6
4 - #   6

Cantus II.   Cantus I.
Ich dan.ke dir, Gott, Ich dan.ke dir, Gott.

Altus: Ich danke dir, Gott. Ich danke dir, Gott.
Cantus II.
Ich dan.ke dir, Gott.

Ich dan.ke dir, Gott.

6   #   #   b   #   b   #5   #   #   (6)   #

17

19

20

21

ken.net mei.ne See _ le wohl, er.ken.net mei.ne See _ _ le wohl.

Ich dan.ke dir, Gott, ich dan.ke dir, Gott.

22

Georg Christoph Bach (1642–1697)

G EORG CHRISTOPH belongs to the branch of the family which produced the greatest among the Bachs. His career varied from those of his contemporary kinsmen in that he served as cantor, thus having teaching duties in addition to the musical ones. He seems to have had a certain literary gift, for we know that he wrote poems in German as well as in Latin. After working for twenty years in the town of Themar, in 1688 Georg Christoph left his native Thuringia to settle down in the province of Franconia, having been appointed cantor in the town of Schweinfurt. Here he established a new center of Bach musicians, and his descendants continued to serve in the town up to 1755. After he had moved to Franconia, his two younger brothers, the twins Johann Christoph and Johann Ambrosius (father of Sebastian), came to visit him for his birthday, an incident which pleased Georg Christoph so much that he celebrated the family reunion in a cantata on the words of Psalm 133, "Behold, how good and how pleasant it is for brethren to dwell together in unity," which, as the only work by this composer, has been preserved in the "Alt-Bachisches Archiv." The title page has the following inscription:

> Trigae Fratrum Germanorum BACHIORUM nempè CONCORDIA florens firma suavis è Psalmo CXXXIII demonstrata et musicè exornata. 2 Tenor: Basso et Violino, 3 Violdigamb: continuo à fratrum natu maximo Georgio Christophoro Bachio. Svvinfurt. Cant. Anno MDCLXXXIX d. 6. Septembris cum illo ipso die Dei gratia implevisset annos 47
>
> [The triple team of the German Bach brothers and its flourishing, sweet, and firm concord, demonstrated with the help of Psalm 133 and adorned by music for two tenors, bass, violin, three viole da gamba, and continuo by the eldest brother, Georg Christoph Bach, cantor in Schweinfurt, on the sixth of September 1689, on which day he reached with the help of God his forty-seventh year.]

This inscription is attractively illustrated in water colors — probably by the hand of the composer — with pictures of three objects which are of symbolic significance: a three-leafed clover which represents the flourishing concord, a triangle with three rings to denote sweetness, and finally a padlock uniting three chains to emphasize firmness. Symbolism, so dear to the baroque mind, also plays an impor-

GEORG CHRISTOPH BACH (1642–1697)

tant part in the composition. Georg Christoph not only uses three solo voices (two tenors and one bass); there are three viols employed and three entrances of each theme. The cantata's pleasing instrumental "praeludium," consisting of three sections (measures 1–15, 16–21, 22–31), has been incorporated into our anthology together with the beginning of the vocal section.

The composition shows solid craftsmanship but not too much inspiration, qualities which may have been typical of his music. Georg Christoph apparently did not reach the high artistic level to be found in the works of Johann and Heinrich; and from all the information we are able to obtain, we feel inclined to assume that creative abilities lay comparatively dormant in this branch of the family until Johann Sebastian stepped in.

The excerpt of the German psalm reproduced here reads according to the King James version:

> Behold, how good and how pleasant it is for brethren to dwell together in unity.

SOURCE OF COMPOSITION REPRODUCED HERE: (Schneider) *RD*, vol. II, p. 22.

BIBLIOGRAPHY

K. Geiringer, pp. 63–65.
M. Schneider in *RD*, vol. II, p. 5.
P. Spitta, vol. I, p. 155.
C. Stapf, "Die Themarer Bachs" in *Johann Sebastian Bach in Thüringen*. Weimar, 1950.

Georg Christoph Bach (1642–1697)

Siehe, wie fein und lieblich

Cantata

25

26

Tenore I, II

Sie - he, wie fein, wie fein und lieb - lich ist, wie

Basso

Sie - he, wie fein, wie fein und lieb - lich ist, wie

Sie - he, wie fein, wie fein und lieb - lich ist, wie

27

Johann Christoph Bach (1642–1703)

JOHANN CHRISTOPH magnificently continued the artistic tradition established by his father, Heinrich. Christoph's mother, Eva Hoffmann, also came from a clan of gifted town musicians, and the combination of these heritages produced the most significant Bach composer before Sebastian. Like his ancestors he held the same position throughout his life, serving as organist in Eisenach. He was not happy in the small provincial town, and numerous reports preserved testify to his constant financial difficulties and to the restlessness which drove him from one domicile to another. The city fathers of the tiny principality did not care for his style of living or for his independent spirit and lack of humility in intercourse with his superiors. Yet when he was offered another position at the city of Schweinfurt, they refused to let him go, being well aware that the quarrelsome organist made an important contribution to Eisenach's musical life. J. Christoph was married to Elisabeth Wedemann, who belonged to a somewhat higher social sphere, her father being a town clerk and syndic of Arnstadt. This may have contributed to Christoph's ceaseless attempts to establish less humble living conditions for his family, attempts which in those times could not but involve him in debts.

In many respects — though not in the handling of his financial affairs — the composer's personality foreshadows that of Sebastian, who showed, however, more fighting spirit and strength of character. Artistically there was an unusually close tie between these two men. Sebastian may have learned the rudiments of organ playing from J. Christoph before he left Eisenach at the age of ten. Anyway it is highly significant that the famous specifications for the remodeling of the Mühlhausen organ, which Sebastian submitted in 1708, are similar to those which J. Christoph drafted eleven years earlier for the reconstruction of the Eisenach organ. In both cases, the city fathers were impressed by the expert advice of their organist and followed it faithfully. As a creative artist, too, J. Christoph exercised great influence on his second cousin; features of his "Sarabande with Twelve Variations" are to be found in Sebastian's "Goldberg Variations," and it is noteworthy that some of J. Christoph's works were for a long time ascribed to the Thomas Cantor.

JOHANN CHRISTOPH BACH (1642–1703)

While J. Christoph's contemporary kinsmen did not get on too well with him, resenting his lack of thrift and economical management, later Bachs held him in the greatest esteem. He was described as "profound" by Sebastian and as "the great and expressive composer" by Philipp Emanuel, who, incidentally, used one of J. Christoph's motets in a composition of his own. J. N. Forkel, the first Bach biographer, tells us of a visit he paid to Philipp Emanuel: "It is still quite fresh in my remembrance how good-naturedly the old man [Emanuel] smiled at me at the most remarkable and hazardous passages when he once gave me the pleasure in Hamburg of letting me hear some of those old pieces [by J. Christoph]." The respect the Bachs felt for the Eisenach organist accounts for the fact that a somewhat larger number of his compositions have been preserved. Apart from a prelude and fugue for organ, we have forty-four of his chorale preludes, two sets of variations for harpsichord, two arias (hymns) for four voices, eight motets, one dialogue, and five cantatas.

J. Christoph's musical language is bold, imaginative, and tremendously expressive, drawing on countless shades of emotion from heart-rending sadness to robust humor. We find among his output some works which appear to be fervent personal documents, such as the solo cantatas "Ach, dass ich Wassers g'nug hätte" and "Wie bist Du denn o Gott," and others which display epic monumentality and grandeur.

One of the finest instrumental works of J. Christoph is the "Praeludium et Fuga" in E flat major, reproduced in our anthology. It was for a long time attributed to Sebastian Bach, and thus slipped into the edition of the Bach Gesellschaft. Although the volume contains some fine compositions by the Thomas Cantor, Christoph's work can hold its own even in so exacting a neighborhood. The piece, which reveals the brilliant toccata style of South German artists such as Johann Jakob Froberger, begins and ends with a free fantasy giving the organist a chance to display his technical skill through runs and arpeggios. The middle section consists of a solidly constructed four-part fugue on a chromatically descending theme. This mixture of well-planned contrapuntal elaboration and free play of imagination produces as fine an example of keyboard music as can be found in seventeenth-century Germany.

The cantata for St. Michael's day, "Es erhub sich ein Streit," is introduced here to demonstrate Christoph's skill in handling larger groups of performers. It should be particularly interesting to American music lovers because the German edition of the work is extremely rare, and is missing from most of the libraries in this country. The work uses as a text Revelation 12: 7–12, and has a certain resemblance to a cantata by Andreas Hammerschmidt. It is written in no less than

JOHANN CHRISTOPH BACH (1642–1703)

twenty-two parts, consisting of two violins, four violas, four trumpets, timpani, and continuo (bassoon and organ), as well as two five-part choruses, one comprising the solo singers, the *favoriti* or *concertae*, the other the accompanying larger body of singers, the *ripieni* or *capella*. In Christoph's monumental setting a brief instrumental introduction, the "Sonata," is followed by a most unusual duet for two basses, which announces in an ominous-sounding canon the beginning of the war in heaven. Gradually trumpets join in, and finally the full body of sound is let loose to produce a breath-taking description of the gigantic struggle between the forces of darkness and of light. In this powerful alfresco picture the triad of C is used exclusively through more than fifty measures. The variety is greater in the second section, when the "loud voice in heaven" proclaims the victory of Christ; and a glorious antiphonal piece in which the two choruses exchange exclamations of joy brings the work to a jubilant close.

This cantata was well known in the Bach family, and it is the only composition by J. Christoph which Forkel, through information from Emanuel Bach, mentions by name. Sebastian may have been inspired by it to write his cantatas No. 19 ("Es erhub sich ein Streit") and No. 50 ("Nun ist das Heil"). It is interesting to note that while the Thomas Cantor felt it advisable to treat the text from Revelation in two individual compositions, his son J. Christoph Friedrich reverted to the method of the older master and based his cantata "Michael's Sieg" on both sections of the text.

The text of this German cantata reads according to the King James version:

> And there was war in heaven: Michael and his angels fought against the dragon; and the dragon fought and his angels,
> And prevailed not; neither was their place found any more in heaven.
> And the great dragon was cast out, that old serpent, called the Devil, and Satan, which deceiveth the whole world; he was cast out into the earth, and his angels were cast out with him.
> And I heard a loud voice saying in heaven, Now is come salvation, and strength, and the kingdom of our God, and the power of his Christ: for the accuser of our brethren is cast down, which accused them before our God day and night.
> And they overcame him by the blood of the Lamb, and by the word of their testimony; and they loved not their lives unto the death.
> Therefore rejoice, ye heavens, and ye that dwell in them.

SOURCE OF COMPOSITIONS REPRODUCED HERE

"Praeludium et Fuga": *BG*, vol. XXXVI, no. 12.
"Es erhub sich ein Streit": MS in Westdeutsche Bibliothek, Marburg, copy of a later date in Gesellschaft der Musikfreunde, Vienna.

JOHANN CHRISTOPH BACH (1642–1703)

BIBLIOGRAPHY

R. Benecke in *MGG*, pp. 954–956.
K. Geiringer, pp. 30–37, 47–62.
F. Rollberg, "Johann Christoph Bach," *Zeitschrift f. Musikwissenschaft*, 1928.
F. Schäfer, "Der Organist Johann Christoph Bach und die Eisenacher Münze," *Luginsland*, 1929.
O. Schumm, "Hof- und Stadtorganist J. Christoph Bach zu Eisenach," *Luginsland*, 1927.
P. Spitta, vol. I, pp. 40–51, 73–96, 100–107; vol. II, pp. 409, 716.
C. S. Terry in *Grove*, pp. 289–290.

Thematic catalog by M. Schneider in *BJ*, 1907, pp. 132–177.

CURRENT EDITIONS OF OTHER WORKS

Works for Clavier and Organ

"Sarabande duodecies variat." (Riemann). Leipzig: Steingräber.
"Aria Eberliniana" (Freyse), Neue Bach Gesellschaft, vol. 39, no. 2, 1940.
"44 Choräle zum Präambulieren" (Fischer), *BV*.

Cantatas

"Ach, dass ich Wassers g'nug hätte" (Schneider). B & H, 1911.
"Wie bist du denn, o Gott" (Seiffert), *DDT*, 2. Folge, vol. VI, no. 1, p. 125.
"Meine Freundin, du bist schön" (Schneider), *RD*, vol. II, p. 91.
"Die Furcht des Herren" (Schneider), *RD*, vol. II, p. 72.

Arias for Four Voices

"Es ist nun aus" and "Mit Weinen hebt sichs an" (Schneider), *RD*, vol. I, pp. 91, 93.

Motets

"Der Mensch, vom Weibe geboren" (Schneider), *RD*, vol. I, p. 95.
"Sei getreu" (Schneider), *RD*, vol. I, p. 98.
"Der Gerechte" (Geiringer). New York: Schirmer, 1941.
"Ich lasse dich nicht" (Geiringer). New York: Schirmer, 1941.
"Unseres Herzens Freude" (Straube). B & H, 1924.
"Lieber Herr Gott" (Junk). B & H, 1922.
"Herr nun lässest du deinen Diener" (Junk). B & H, 1922.
"Fürchte dich nicht" (Junk). B & H, 1922.

Johann Christoph Bach (1642–1703)

Praeludium et Fuga

For Clavier

Praeludium.

*) Suggested performance.

Fuga. Allegro

34

Johann Christoph Bach (1642–1703)

Es erhub sich ein Streit

Cantata

36

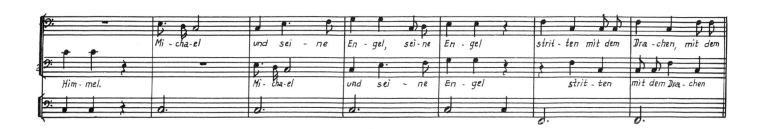

37

38

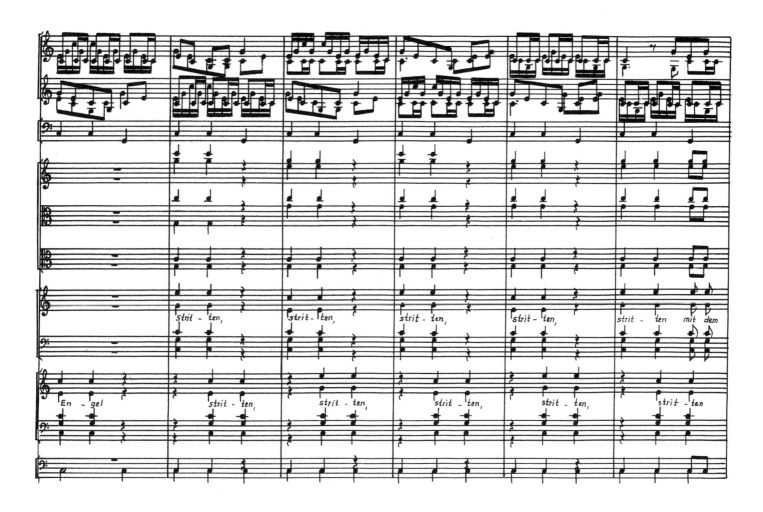

Sinfonia

44

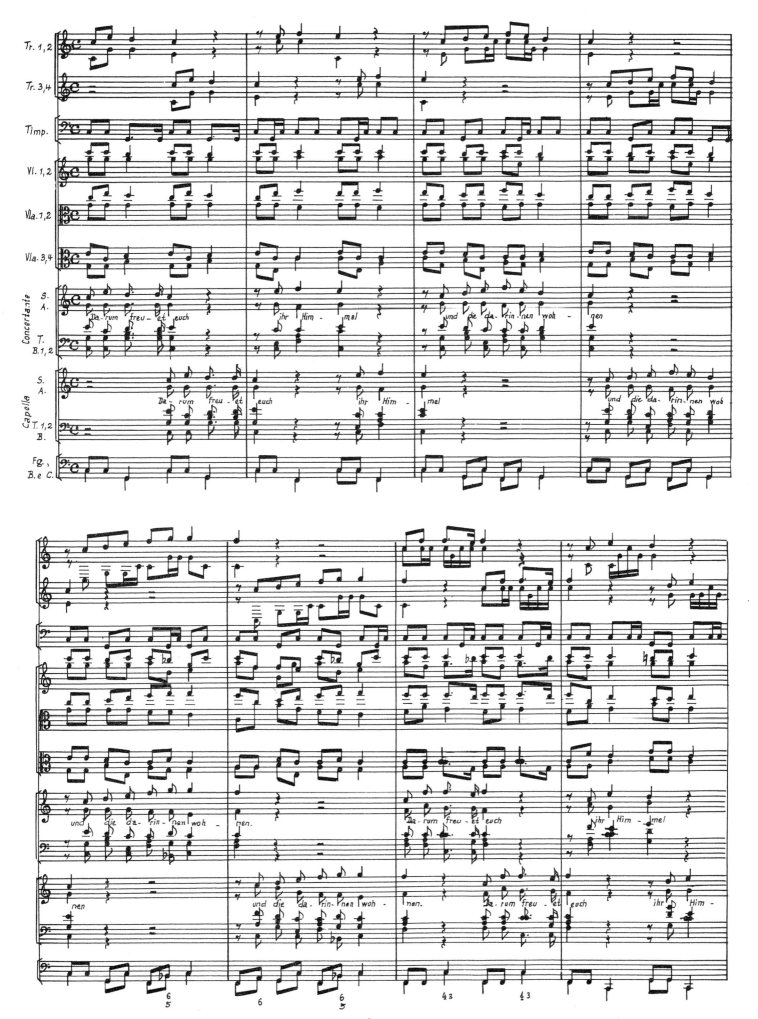

49

51

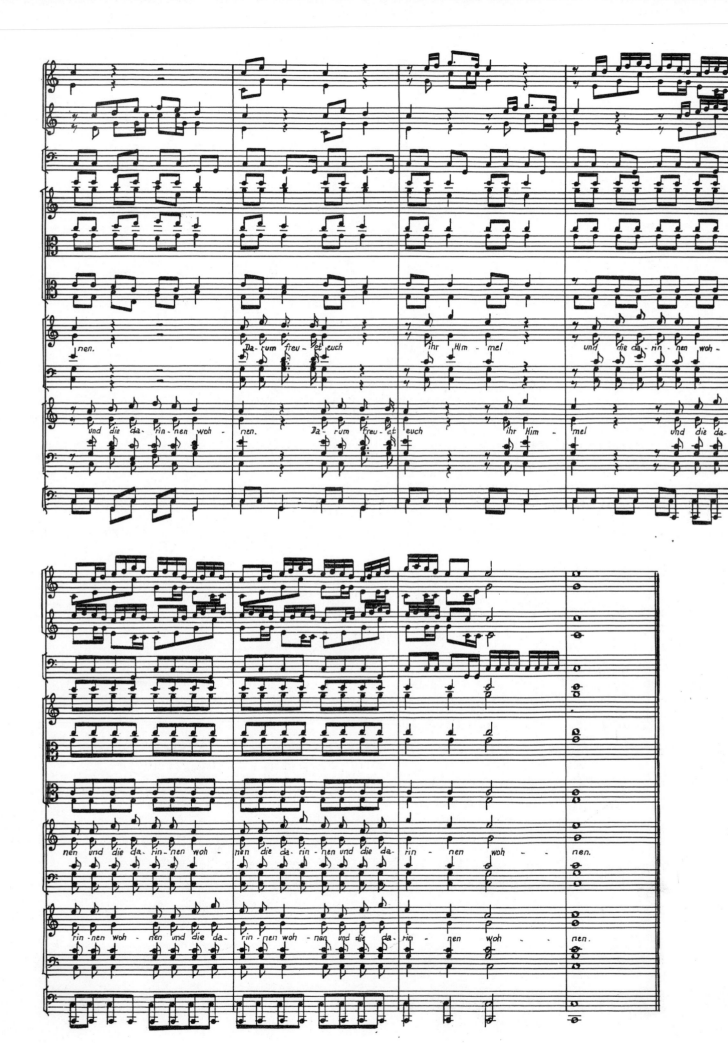

Johann Michael Bach (1648–1694)

JOHANN MICHAEL, younger brother of J. Christoph, served as organist and municipal clerk in the little town of Gehren near Arnstadt, where he seems to have established more satisfactory relations with the authorities than did the Eisenach organist. In other respects he followed closely in his elder brother's footsteps; like him, he married two years after receiving his appointment, and he chose Catharina Wedemann, a sister of J. Christoph's wife. Although he led a less harassed existence, he was not granted so long a life as his elder brother and his father. He died at the age of forty-six, leaving five unmarried daughters, the youngest of whom, called Maria Barbara, was thirteen years later to marry her cousin J. Sebastian.

While most of the Bachs by tradition were expert craftsmen in the field of organ construction, J. Michael also showed great skill in building stringed instruments and clavichords. A seal of his has been preserved which, significantly, displays two bows and a pair of violin scrolls.

By a strange coincidence sixteen vocal compositions by J. Michael have come to us, exactly the amount of his brother's output in this field which was handed down to posterity. In addition we know eight organ chorales and one set of variations for the clavier. The majority of J. Michael's works, while revealing great talent, are not so powerful and moving as Johann Christoph's music. He seems to have been particularly gifted as an instrumental composer, but unfortunately his clavier variations are known only through an unreliable arrangement for harmonium; and of his seventy-two organ chorales, which the lexicographer Ernst Ludwig Gerber claims to have owned, only one ninth has been traced so far. In his vocal works, too, concern for the instruments is apparent. For instance, the solo cantata "Es ist ein grosser Gewinn" employs a "quart violino non di grosso grande." This instrument "of the small variety," probably tuned a fourth higher than the ordinary violin, may have been built by J. Michael himself.

As an example of his chorale preludes we have included here "Von Gott will ich nicht lassen" (From God I'll not Be Parted). This is music written strictly for everyday use, avoiding all flights of imagination that might confuse the congregation. Such a piece could not possibly have been subjected to derogatory comments of the kind later bestowed on the organ chorales of Michael's second cousin and son-in-law, Sebastian Bach. After a short introduction the hymn tune is played in long-sustained notes by the top voice, against a background provided by two fast-moving lower voices. This type of chorale prelude was in general use in the small churches of the Bachs' Thuringian homeland.

On a higher level is our second example, Michael's arrangement of "Wenn wir in höchsten Nöthen seyn" (When We Are Troubled Through and Through), in which the composer leans on the style of an older master, the great Halle composer Samuel Scheidt (1587–1654). This is a set of three chorale variations, the first of which is again in three parts with the melody in the top voice, though in an ornamented form. In the second variation the tune is given to the middle part and surrounded by a supporting pedal bass and a freely invented melody. Most attractive is the third variation, in which the chorale melody, once more entrusted to the upper part, is engulfed by swiftly moving sixteenth notes. A delightful tone picture is achieved, creating the impression of lightness and release from life's burden.

One of the most moving compositions by Michael Bach is his motet for double chorus "Herr, ich warte auf dein Heil" (Lord, I Wait for Thy Salvation). Here the second chorus sings words from the Bible, while the first chorus again and again interrupts with a chorale. Soon, however, a deep longing for death unites the two groups, and they join in a final supplication to the Lord to take the soul to heaven. The simplicity of this piece, with its plain harmonization of the chorale melody and its naïve pictorialism (such as long-drawn-out melismas on the word "wait"), provides it with a genuine warmth and emotional impact found only in the finest motet compositions of the time.

The text reads in a free English translation:

> Lord, I wait for Thy salvation, o come and take me.
> O with what longing I await the time when Thou, o Lord, wilt come and lead me out of this distress of my heart to Thee in heaven.

SOURCE OF COMPOSITIONS REPRODUCED HERE

"Von Gott will ich nicht lassen" and "Wenn wir in höchsten Nöthen seyn": MSS in Deutsche Staatsbibliothek, Berlin, Sammlung Dröbs.
"Herr, ich warte auf dein Heil": (Schneider) *RD*, vol. I, p. 84.

BIBLIOGRAPHY

R. Benecke in *MGG*, pp. 920–921.
K. Geiringer, pp. 38–47.
W. Martini, "Die Gehrener Bache" in *Johann Sebastian Bach in Thüringen*. Weimar, 1950.
P. Spitta, vol. I, pp. 37–40, 51–53, 58–73.

JOHANN MICHAEL BACH (1648–1694)

C. S. Terry in *Grove*, pp. 290–291.

F. Wiegand, "Die Arnstädter Bache" in *Johann Sebastian Bach und seine Verwandten in Arnstadt*. Arnstadt, 1950.

Thematic catalog by M. Schneider in *BJ*, 1907, pp. 109–132.

CURRENT EDITIONS OF OTHER WORKS

Organ Chorales

"Wenn mein Stündlein" in Ritter, *Geschichte des Orgelspiels*. Leipzig, 1884. Vol. II, p. 104.
"Dies sind die heil'gen zehn Gebot" in Ritter, *Orgelfreund*, vol. VI, no. 46.
"In dich hab' ich gehoffet" in *RD*, vol. IX.
"Nun freut euch," *Orgel Journal*, vol. I, p. 7, Mannheim.

Cantatas

"Es ist ein grosser Gewinn" (Schneider). *RD*, vol. II, p. 39.
"Ach wie sehnlich" (Schneider). *RD*, vol. II, p. 46.
"Auf, lasst uns" (Schneider). *RD*, vol. II, p. 49.
"Liebster Jesu" (Schneider). *RD*, vol. II, p. 53.
"Ach bleib bei uns" (Schneider). *RD*, vol. II, p. 61.

Motets

"Unser Leben" (Schneider). *RD*, vol. I, p. 19.
"Das Blut" (Schneider). *RD*, vol. I, p. 22.
"Herr, wenn ich nur" (Schneider). *RD*, vol. I, p. 29.
"Ich weiss" (Geiringer). New York: Schirmer, 1941.
"Sei lieber Tag" (Schneider). *RD*, vol. I, p. 39.
"Nun hab ich" (Schneider). *RD*, vol. I, p. 47.
"Halt, was du hast" (Schneider). *RD*, vol. I, p. 53.
"Fürchtet euch nicht" (Schneider). *RD*, vol. I, p. 62.
"Herr, du lässest" (Schneider). *RD*, vol. I, p. 68.
"Dem Menschen ist" (Schneider). *RD*, vol. I, p. 75.

Johann Michael Bach (1648–1694)

Von Gott will ich nicht lassen

Chorale Prelude for Organ

56

Johann Michael Bach (1648–1694)

Wenn wir in höchsten Nöthen seyn   Chorale Variations for Organ

I

II

III

Johann Michael Bach (1648–1694)

Herr, ich warte auf dein Heil

Motet

63

66

Johann Nicolaus Bach (1669–1753)

JOHANN NICOLAUS was the eldest son of the great Johann Christoph. It is interesting to note that the talent exhibited by his grandfather and father was still flourishing in the third generation, an occurrence which was not too frequent even in the Bach family. Nicolaus spent most of his life in the university town of Jena, where he served as organist and academic music director. Jena's salubrious air was generally praised; it may have contributed to Nicolaus' excellent health and enabled him to reach the ripe age of eighty-four. Nicolaus was the first of the Bach musicians to travel to Italy, which offered him important artistic stimulation. As a youth he may have received some training from his uncle, J. Michael — at any rate, he was, like the Gehren organist, interested in the building of instruments, and his own inventions in this field enjoyed a high reputation. He devised several improvements for the organ and the harpsichord and constructed a lute which was played with the help of a keyboard. We find enthusiastic comments about all these achievements in the treatises of the musicologist Jakob Adlung, who was Nicolaus' pupil. The composer naturally felt great concern about the organ entrusted to him in Jena, and he was responsible for a thorough reconstruction of it which was so successful that the instrument remained in use up to our own century.

Apart from a rather insignificant organ composition, only two of his works are known to have survived. One is a short Mass consisting of a Kyrie and Gloria only. In the Kyrie we notice influences of the melodic language of North Italian composers. The Gloria, however, presents a very different picture. Here Nicolaus employs four verses of a Protestant chorale sung in German, thus intermingling German and Latin texts, Catholic and Protestant elements. The work seems to have greatly influenced younger members of the family: the Thomas Cantor resorted to a similar method when he introduced a Lutheran chorale tune as a *cantus firmus* in the Kyrie of his Mass in F major; and Johann Ernst Bach, a member of the following generation, employed the melody of a Protestant hymn throughout the two sections of his Mass, using its first half in the Kyrie and its second in the Gloria.

Nicolaus' second larger work is the comical cantata "Der Jenaische Wein- und

JOHANN NICOLAUS BACH (1669–1753)

Bierrufer." It was probably written for the Collegium Musicum of the Jena University, and we can well imagine that it was acted on the stage, creating hilarious response from fellow students. The hero of this work lived in the composer's time and was therefore well known to the audience; his actual function in Jena was to notify the citizens of the opening of a fresh cask of beer or wine in the tavern. In this *Singspiel* two freshmen recently arrived in Jena are edged on by an innkeeper to enter into an argument with the old beer-crier. Tempers are frayed and abusive words used but ultimately peace is restored, and a tercet in praise of Jena concludes the little burlesque. The orchestra consists of only two violins and continuo, and ensemble numbers occur merely at the beginning and the end. Such economy was typical of the comic opera of the time, and Nicolaus' work displays a certain resemblance to compositions of the contemporary Hamburg school.

The final trio of the *Singspiel*, a kind of drinking song, has been included in our anthology because it reveals the gay and melodious style, inspired by folksongs, which Nicolaus liked to use. To some extent the number reminds us also of Sebastian's music, whose "Coffee Cantata" and "Peasant Cantata" contain rather similar pieces.

The text of the final trio reads in a free English translation:

> In Jena strange things happen, as all the world well knows.
> One often looks for pleasure there, but does not always find it; so everyone tries to devise something new.
> In Jena strange things happen, as all the world well knows.
> One often seeks contentment in beer and new-made wine, and if the day is all too short, one keeps right on through the night.
> In Jena strange things happen, as all the world well knows.

SOURCE OF COMPOSITION REPRODUCED HERE: "Der Jenaische Wein- und Bierrufer" (Stein). B & H, 1921.

BIBLIOGRAPHY

R. Benecke in *MGG*, pp. 921–922.
K. Geiringer, pp. 87–96.
H. Koch, "Der Jenaer Bach" in *Bach in Thüringen.* Berlin, 1950.
F. Rollberg, "Aus der Heimat und dem Familienkreis des Jenaischen Organisten Johann Nicolaus Bach," *Jenaische Zeitung*, no. 88, 1933.
P. Spitta, vol. I, pp. 131–140.
C. S. Terry in *Grove*, p. 290.
E. Wennig, *Chronik des musikalischen Lebens der Stadt Jena.* Jena, 1937.

CURRENT EDITION OF OTHER WORK

Mass in e (Junk). B & H, 1920.

Johann Nicolaus Bach (1669–1753)

In Jena geht es wunderlich

From Cantata *Der Jenaische Wein- und Bierrufer*

weiss die gan - ze Welt.

1. Man su.chet öf.ters sei.ne Lust und fin.det sol.che nicht, doch

2. Oft sucht man die Ver.gnüg.lich.keit bei fri.schem Bier und Wein, und

1. hat auch wohl des An.dern Brust was neu.es aus.ge.dicht, was neu.es aus.ge.dicht. In

2. hat man nicht bei Ta.ge Zeit, so kann's des A.bends sein, so kann's des A.bends sein.

Johann Bernhard Bach (1676–1749)

JOHANN BERNHARD was a grandson of Johann and thus related to Sebastian through both his grandfather and his grandmother. His father served as director of the Erfurt town band, but Bernhard won in young years such a reputation as a fine organist that he was offered a position outside of Thuringia in the town of Magdeburg. Apparently he felt anxious to live again in his native province, for when on the death of the great Johann Christoph the organist's position in Eisenach became vacant, he decided to leave Magdeburg and to accept the Eisenach appointment, which he retained until his death.

While it is mainly the vocal output of the older Bachs that has survived, we know only instrumental works by Bernhard. Their preservation was again due to kinsmen. Sebastian performed Bernhard's four orchestral suites and wrote out some of the parts. In addition Bernhard's pupil and relative (on the Lämmerhirt side), the eminent organist and scholar Johann Gottfried Walther, copied his teacher's keyboard compositions: nine chorale preludes, two fugues, and a chaconne.

Bernhard's orchestral suites were probably destined for the concerts given at the court of his patron, the music-loving Duke Johann Wilhelm of Eisenach. These performances reached a high standard under the direction of the gifted Georg Philipp Telemann, who served the Eisenach court for four years and greatly stimulated the artistic work of his colleagues.

Bernhard's delightful Suite in G minor for solo violin and strings has been made available through a recent reprint. We have therefore chosen for our anthology an unpublished Suite in D major, presenting six of its movements (two of its three "Caprices" were omitted). The work reveals a certain leaning towards French tradition, a common tendency in the German orchestral suite of the time. The composer employs for the individual parts the old French terms *dessus, haute contre*, and *taille*, which indicate a range rather than an instrument. In addition to dances bearing French names, the suite comprises also character pieces headed "La Joye" and "Caprice."

The work starts in the typical manner with a broadly contoured French *ouverture*, consisting of a majestic first section, a skillfully wrought fugue in faster motion, and a concluding section which reiterates the ideas of the slow beginning. A spirited "Marche" is followed by two gay "Passepieds," the second of which conforms to the traditional idea of a trio since it is written throughout for three voices. The "Air" with the tempo indication "Lentement" serves as a slow movement, the following "La Joye" as a kind of scherzo. The concluding movement inscribed "Caprice" resembles in its form the introductory overture. It starts with a slow section in dotted rhythms and continues with a fast fugue (a formal scheme not to be found in the two other, less elaborate "Caprices"). This idea of Bernhard's to erect solid pillars both at the beginning and at the end of the suite is quite significant and rather unusual.

SOURCE OF COMPOSITION REPRODUCED HERE: MS parts of the eighteenth century in Westdeutsche Bibliothek, Marburg. FP.

BIBLIOGRAPHY

R. Benecke in *MGG*, p. 918.
K. Geiringer, pp. 98–101.
H. Kühn, "Vier Organisten Eisenachs aus bachischem Geschlecht" in *Bach in Thüringen*. Berlin, 1950.
P. Spitta, vol. I, pp. 23–26; vol. II, p. 144.

CURRENT EDITIONS OF OTHER WORKS

Fugue for Clavier or Organ in F (Riemann). Leipzig: Steingräber.
Fugue for Clavier or Organ in D, in Ritter, *Geschichte des Orgelspiels*. Leipzig, 1884. Vol. II, p. 106.
"Christ lag in Todesbanden," organ chorale, and "Nun freut euch," organ chorale (Frotscher). *RD*, vol. 9.
"Du Friedefürst," organ chorale. Straube, *Choralvorspiele*, No. 3. Leipzig, 1907.
Ouverture No. 1, in g (Fareanu). B & H, 1920.

Johann Bernhard Bach (1676–1749)

Ouverture in D

For Instrumental Ensemble

75

76

(Lentement)

Marche

78

Passepied I

unisono

Passepied II

Air
Lentement

80

La Joye

Caprice
(Lentement)

Vitement

tasto solo

83

Johann Ludwig Bach (1677–1731)

JOHANN LUDWIG belongs to a branch of the family about whose early history we know very little. Musical talent revealed itself in Ludwig's father, who served as a teacher and cantor in various small towns of Thuringia. Ludwig received a good education, and from the age of twenty-two on he lived at the court of the Duke of Saxe-Meiningen, where he worked as cantor and master of the ducal pages until, under the reign of the succeeding sovereign, he was appointed director of the court orchestra. Having then more leisure, he composed works of great significance for his group of performers, and music assumed a dominant position in the life of the small court. Ludwig seems to have been proficient in painting, too, as he gave instruction in the art to the princes. This talent appeared to a much greater extent in one of his sons and a grandson, who both developed into most successful painters in addition to being court organists. Although Ludwig himself died at the age of fifty-four, his descendants exhibited unusual health and vitality — his grandson Johann Philipp reached the age of ninety-four. The Meiningen Bach line is still in existence, and its present representative, Mr. Paul Bach of Eisenach, is a gifted amateur painter and cellist.

No member of the Bach family is known so little yet deserves to be known so much as Johann Ludwig. An orchestral suite and one motet, presented in an arrangement which obscures the intentions of the composer, are all that have so far been printed of the thirty-odd masterworks, mainly cantatas and motets, that have been preserved — in spite of the fact that Sebastian Bach was so impressed by the work of his kinsman that he copied no less than eighteen of Ludwig's cantatas so as to be able to perform them in Leipzig.

The music of the Meiningen Bach is lyric rather than dramatic in character. Most of his compositions are conceived on a fairly large scale and display an almost Italian beauty of melodic lines and a keen sense for coloristic effects. Although the texture of the music is predominantly homophonic, there is no lack of variety in these scores. Ludwig's cantatas and motets are powerful and truly inspired pieces whose emotional fervor is balanced by the composer's great skill in handling the large groups of performers he likes to use.

As an example of his motet style we have included an excerpt from "Gott sey uns gnädig," using Psalm 67 as a text. It is written for two four-part choruses of mixed voices, to which a separate bass voice is added. While the two groups are engaged in an antiphonal presentation of the psalm text, the ninth voice at first sings ascending and descending scale passages in the manner of a slow *cantus firmus*. It would seem possible that we have here an example of typical baroque pictorialism, inspired by the story of Jacob's ladder on which angels ascended and descended from earth to heaven (Genesis 28: 12); Ludwig may have inserted it to symbolize the close connection of mundane and divine matters. Later the ponderous *cantus firmus* gives way to fast-moving jubilant melismas intoned by the odd bass voice and accompanied by joyful exclamations of the choruses. Eventually the three basses join forces to proclaim to the strains of the Magnificat tune the triumphant message: "God shall bless us and all the ends of the earth shall fear Him."

The text of our excerpt reads according to the King James version:

> Let the people praise thee, O God; let all the people praise thee.
> O let the nations be glad and sing for joy: for thou shalt judge the people righteously, and govern the nations upon earth. Selah.
> God shall bless us; and all the ends of the earth shall fear him.

Our second example is taken from the extensive funeral cantata based on verses 16–19 of Psalm 116 which Ludwig composed for his beloved patron, Duke Ernst Ludwig of Meiningen (d. 1724). According to the custom of the time the sovereign himself wrote part of the text for his funeral music. The cantata is conceived in three extensive sections and uses throughout two four-part choruses, each accompanied by its own group of instruments. In the second section, part of which we are reproducing here, strings and harpsichord support the first chorus, wood wind and harpsichord the second. At first a soprano and an alto proclaim their desire to leave the earth and to seek Jesus; then a tenor movingly expresses his longing for the sublime city of Jerusalem, while the chorus quietly sings a hymn in praise of the "Citadel of Heaven." The last section represents paradise, where, exhorted by the bass singer, the two choruses burst into a tremendous "Halleluja," which intermingles with the strains of the hymn tune.

A free translation of the text of the funeral music reads:

> So world farewell, I am weary of thee. I am looking for my Jesus only; in Him I find true peace; there I may live in bliss. I would leave this world, join God in His great heavenly home.
> Jerusalem, I am yearning for thee, but thou art not to be found in this world. Up

JOHANN LUDWIG BACH (1677–1731)

there thou art, there I will shine. In the heavenly abode of my God I seek only the position of keeper of the gate.

Jerusalem, thou sublime city, would God I were there. My yearning heart has such great longing and does not remain with me any more; far over hills and dale, far over level fields, it soars everywhere and hastens out of this world.

Then I will sing Halleluja, praised be the mighty God. Halleluja shall ever resound to mighty God who helps in time of need. All join in Halleluja.

When at last I have arrived in fair paradise, with greatest joy my heart is filled, my lips with praise and exultation. A pure Halleluja is sung in the beauty of holiness, a lovely Hosanna without end to all eternity.

SOURCE OF COMPOSITIONS REPRODUCED HERE

"Gott sey uns gnädig": Deutsche Staatsbibliothek, Berlin (P. 329). FP.
Funeral Music: Westdeutsche Bibliothek, Marburg (P. 398). FP.

BIBLIOGRAPHY

P. Bach, "Die Meininger Bache" in *Johann Sebastian Bach in Thüringen*. Weimar, 1950.
K. Geiringer, pp. 104–118.
C. Mühlfeld, *Die herzogliche Hofkapelle in Meiningen*. Meiningen, 1910.
P. Spitta, vol. I, pp. 10, 389, 574–582; vol. III, p. 263.

Ludwig's cantatas are listed in *BG*, vol. 41, pp. 275–276.

CURRENT EDITIONS OF OTHER WORKS

Suite for Orchestra in G (Friedrich). Vienna: Universal-Edition, 1939.
"Uns ist ein Kind geboren," motet (Moser). Leipzig: Kistner & Siegel, 1930.

Johann Ludwig Bach (1677–1731)

Es danken dir, Gott

From Motet *Gott sey uns gnädig*

89

90

94

Johann Ludwig Bach (1677–1731)

Drum Welt ade

From *Trauer Music*

95

ich will aus die-ser Welt hin-aus zu Gott in sein gross, sein gross Him-mels-haus,zu Gott in sein gross Him-mels-haus.

ich will aus die-ser Welt hin-aus zu Gott in sein gross Him-mels-haus,zu Gott in sein gross Him-mels-haus.

Tenore Coro I

Je-ru-sa-lem, Je-ru-sa-lem ich thu ver-

*) The lowest part, written in the manuscript in Alto clef, is obviously meant for Alto Oboe (Oboe da Caccia or English Horn).
**) To save space the continuo parts of the two choruses were written in a single line, those of the first chorus with stems up, those of the second chorus with stems down.

40
pran-gen, dort o-ben ists, dort o-ben ists. In mei-nes Got-tes Him-mels-
so gross Ver-lan-gen hat und ist nicht mehr bey mir.
zelt, in mei-nes Got-tes Him-mels-zelt, in mei-nes Got-tes Him-mels-haus ich
Weit ü-ber Berg und Tha-le, weit ü-ber
45
nur das Pfört-ner-amt, ich nur das Pfört-ner-amt such aus, das Pfört-ner-amt,
fla-ches Feld schwingt es sich ü-ber al-

in mei-nes Got-tes Him-mels-haus ich nur das Pfört-ner-amt, ich nur das Pfört-ner-amt such

le und eilt aus die-ser Welt.

le und eilt aus die-ser Welt.

(Allegro)

Tenore Coro I

aus.

Flauti

e Viol.

Vla.

Basso Coro I

Dann werd ich Hal-le-lu-ja sin-gen.

Ge-lo-bet sey, ge-lo-bet

(Allegro)

I

Fl. e

Viol.

Vla.

Basso Coro I

sey, ge-lo-bet sey der gros-se Gott, ge-lo-bet sey der gros-se Gott.

Stets Hal-le-lu-ja soll er-

klin - gen   dem gros - sen Gott, dem gros - sen Gott, dem gros - sen Gott, der hilft aus Noth.

Stimmt al - le an Hal - le - lu - ja, Hal - le - lu - ja, Hal - le - lu - ja, stimmt al - le an, stimmt al - le

Viol. I, II

Coro I   Vla.

S.
A.   an, Hal - le - lu - ja, Hal - le - lu - ja, Hal - le - lu - ja, Hal - le - lu - ja
Coro I
T.
B.

Coro I   3 Fl., 2 Ob.

S.
A.   Hal - le - lu - ja, Hal - le - lu -
Coro II
T.
B.

Cemb.

Cont.

101

Stimmt al - le an, stimmt al - le an, Hal -le -lu - ja, Hal -le - lu-ja,

ja.

Hal - le -lu - ja,

ja, Hal - le -lu - ja, Hal -le - lu-ja,

Hal - le - lu - ja, Hal - le -lu -

105

110

106

Wilhelm Friedemann Bach (1710–1784)

FRIEDEMANN, Sebastian's eldest son, was the father's favorite. His first music instruction was based on the little *Clavierbüchlein* which Sebastian wrote for him at Coethen. This interesting document — preserved today by Yale University — contains besides pieces by other composers most of·Sebastian's two- and three-part inventions, as well as twelve preludes which were subsequently included in the *Well-Tempered Clavier*. Friedemann made excellent progress, and the father, convinced of his son's talent, sent the sixteen-year-old to J. G. Graun in Merseburg to study the violin with this famous master. Nevertheless Friedemann's interest remained centered on the keyboard instruments, and he developed into an inspired organist whose feats were often compared to those of his father. After studying at the University of Leipzig, he received in 1733 his first position as organist of the Sophienkirche at Dresden, where he served for thirteen years. This was a fruitful period for the artist. His professional duties took up little time; thus he was able to concentrate on composition, and the nearness of Leipzig made personal as well as artistic contacts with his father possible. The result was a number of valuable works created in Dresden. The position at the Sophienkirche offered, however, no possibilities for promotion, and when Friedemann learned of a vacancy in nearby Halle, he applied for the post. In so doing he closely followed the example of his father, who had thirty years earlier started similar negotiations. Friedemann received the appointment, and on Whitsunday in 1746 he started work as organist and director of music at the highly renowned Liebfrauenkirche, taking over responsibilities which in many ways resembled those of the Thomas Cantor at Leipzig. He retained the post in Halle for eighteen years, but he never succeeded in establishing pleasant relations with his superiors there. At times he tried for another appointment, without ever being able to secure it, and it is significant that the two positions he actually held were both obtained while Sebastian, his best helper and advisor, was still alive. By 1764 the Halle organist had accumulated so much resentment against the lack of cooperation and the narrowmindedness of the city fathers that he suddenly resigned his position. For six years he stayed on at Halle, precariously supporting himself and his family by working as a music teacher. Then he started a wandering existence, looking for positions at Braunschweig, Göttingen, and finally Berlin. He spent the last ten years of his life in the Prussian capital, fighting a desperate struggle against poverty and ill health. Wherever he appeared he at first entranced music lovers by his superb organ playing, but he did not inspire the confidence necessary for appointment to a permanent position; he alienated admirers and friends by his intransigency and his unwillingness to play before influential people or to instruct mediocre pupils.

The life of this eldest son of Sebastian was an unhappy, even a tragic, one. He yearned for an existence which was by no means in keeping with the customs of the time; he wasted his energies in constant fights against the indifference and lack of understanding shown by the people around him. As a composer, too, he felt insufficiently appreciated. After he announced the publication of a series of six clavier sonatas, only the first was actually printed while the rest remained in manuscript owing to the public's lack of interest. Even worse was the fate of his polonaises, which are among his finest contributions; although he announced their completion, he never received enough orders to present them in print. Failures of this kind greatly discouraged him and sapped his creative vigor; consequently his output, which had never been very large, gradually dwindled away.

Thus the number of works he wrote during a life that lasted seventy-four years, just as long as that of Handel or of his own brother Emanuel, was comparatively small. Besides some minor vocal compositions, we know today about two dozen church cantatas, of which only sixteen are original compositions while the remainder are adaptations and arrangements of earlier works. Of greater significance is his instrumental music, which, apart from compositions of doubtful authenticity, comprises the following:

 7 organ chorales
12 fugues for organ or clavier
 9 clavier sonatas
10 clavier fantasias
12 clavier polonaises and other small pieces for clavier
 1 concerto for harpsichord (unaccompanied)
 1 concerto for 2 harpsichords (unaccompanied; in *BG* attributed to J. S. Bach)
 5 concertos for harpsichord and orchestra
 1 concerto for 2 harpsichords and orchestra
 6 sonatas for 2 flutes
 3 sonatas for 2 violas
 2 trios for 2 violins and bass
 2 trios for 2 flutes and bass
 9 symphonies

WILHELM FRIEDEMANN BACH (1710–1784)

Friedemann's compositions, in particular his instrumental works, display the expressive and emotional style characteristic of North German music in the era of sensibility. He likes sudden contrasts and unexpected changes, dramatic and at times even humorous effects. On the other hand the influence of his father's style is unmistakable. His church compositions make ample use of polyphonic devices, and even the homophonic forms prevalent among his instrumental works display a predilection for playful imitations. As a rule he is satisfied to employ a single theme in each movement, and the formal construction of his works points more towards the past than the future.

As an example of Friedemann's chamber music, we are presenting the middle movement and finale from his Sonata in F major for two flutes. This composition was probably written while the composer served in Dresden (1733–1746), where he was on friendly terms with the outstanding flutist, P. G. Buffardin. The two wind instruments are treated as equals. Their parts constantly cross, and Friedemann makes the very best use of the modest means at his disposal. The tragic "Lamentabile" displays a fervor and depth of feeling few composers expressed in his time. The following "Presto," on the other hand, is imbued with an affirmative spirit. It is a gay piece revealing the composer's gift of writing truly idiomatic music.

The "Concerto a Cembalo Concertato, 2 violini, viola e basso" in E flat major, which we present as our second example, remained unfinished. Friedemann seems to have composed it in Halle during the 1750's. While engaged in writing the second movement, he needed an introductory sinfonia for his cantata "Ertönet ihr seligen Völker." He chose the first movement of the E flat concerto, transposing it one tone up and adding two oboes whose parts were derived from that of the solo harpsichord, while the string orchestra remained on the whole unchanged. Friedemann seems to have later on forgotten the original version, which breaks off in the middle of the slow movement. Since this is a very significant work which has never been printed, we reproduce it here from the composer's autograph. The score, which is undated, uses fewer *tutti* passages than Friedemann's earlier works in this field and shows a certain conciseness which is found in the composer's later concertos. Particularly attractive is the slow movement, and it is much to be regretted that this charming piece remained a fragment. The handwriting in the autograph is characteristic of the composer's hasty and impetuous penmanship, which gives a reader trying to decipher the score all kinds of problems to solve. The paper is used most economically, with the orchestral basses written in the same line as the left hand of the harpsichord, the way it is done in our score. Evidently the composer had not forgotten his father's admonition to avoid unnecessary expense.

WILHELM FRIEDEMANN BACH (1710–1784)

SOURCE OF COMPOSITIONS REPRODUCED HERE

Flute Sonata: MS (formerly in Kirnberger's possession, later in Amalienbibliothek) in Universitätsbibliothek, Tübingen (P. 112).

Concerto in E flat: Autograph in Westdeutsche Bibliothek, Marburg (P. 331). FP.

BIBLIOGRAPHY

C. H. Bitter, *C. P. E. und W. F. Bach und deren Brüder*. Berlin, 1868.

F. Blume in *MGG*, pp. 1047–1055.

M. Falck, *Wilhelm Friedemann Bach*. Leipzig, 1913.

K. Geiringer, pp. 303–335.

E. Reeser, *The Sons of Bach*. Stockholm, 1949, pp. 7–24.

Thematic catalog compiled by M. Falck (see above), Appendix, pp. 1–31.

CURRENT EDITIONS OF OTHER WORKS

Works for Organ and Clavier

3 Fugues and 7 Chorale Preludes for Organ (Power Biggs and Weston). New York: Music Press, 1947.

8 Fugues (Niemann). Leipzig: Peters, 1914.

9 Clavier Sonatas (Blume). *NMA*, 1930–1940.

6 Fantasias for Clavier (Banck). Leipzig: Kistner & Siegel, 1881.

3 Fantasias for Clavier (Riemann). Leipzig: Steingräber.

12 Polonaises (Wührer). Vienna: Bundesverlag, 1949–1953.

Short Clavier Compositions (Riemann). Leipzig: Steingräber.

Concertos

Concerto for two Harpsichords [unaccompanied]. *BG*, vol. 43, p. 47.

Concerto in e for Harpsichord and Strings (Upmeyer). Berlin: Vieweg, 1931.

Concertos in a, D, and F for Harpsichord and Strings, arranged for 2 Claviers (Riemann). Leipzig: Steingräber.

Concerto for 2 Claviers and Orchestra in E flat. New York: Public Library.

Chamber Music and Symphony

6 Sonatas for 2 Flutes (Walther). B & H.

3 Sonatas for 2 Violas. Cologne: Tischer & Jagenberg.

Sonata for Violin and Harpsichord in B (Schittler). Munich: Wunderhorn, 1910.

Trio in B flat for 2 Violins and Bass (Riemann). B & H, 1875–1876.

4 Trios for 2 Solo Instruments and Continuo (Seiffert). B & H, 1934.

Sinfonia in d (Schittler). Munich: Wunderhorn, 1910.

Vocal Works

"Lasset uns ablegen," chorus (Weston). B & H, 1912.

"Dies ist der Tag," cantata (Nowak). Leipzig: Musikwissenschaftlicher Verlag, 1937.

"Heilig, heilig," chorus (Schering). Leipzig: Kahnt, 1922.

"Zerbrechet, zerreisset," aria (Schittler). Munich: Wunderhorn-Verlag, 1910.

Wilhelm Friedemann Bach (1710–1784)

Lamentabile and Presto

From Sonata in F for 2 Flutes

113

Wilhelm Friedemann Bach (1710–1784)

Concerto in E flat (unfinished)   For Cembalo Solo and Strings

MS uses various abbreviations unified here to "Vlc." This means: to be played by orchestral basses only and not by clavier.

Carl Philipp Emanuel Bach (1714–1788)

PHILIPP EMANUEL, the second surviving son of Sebastian, led a life very different from that of his elder brother. Endowed with very fine musical gifts, he had the strength of character to develop them fully while freeing himself from the impact of his father's personality. Sebastian was Emanuel's only teacher, and he helped the youth to become one of the foremost clavierists and clavier teachers of his time. Like Friedemann, Emanuel received an academic education, studying law from 1731 to 1738 at the Universities of Leipzig and Frankfurth-on-the-Oder. The choice of the latter institute reveals young Emanuel's striving for independence, and motives of this kind may have been responsible for his going to Berlin after he finished his courses. There he succeeded in arousing the interest of the music-loving Prussian crown prince, Frederick (subsequently King Frederick "the Great"), who engaged him for his own orchestra at Ruppin. When Frederick succeeded to the throne, Emanuel stayed in his service; he had the honor of acting as accompanist when the new king performed his first solo on the flute, the monarch's favorite instrument, and he retained the position as royal clavierist up to 1768. Emanuel frequently thought of changing his position because there was a great deal he did not like in his work with the autocratic monarch, who had not too much appreciation for his clavierist's creative achievements. To leave Berlin was impossible, however, without special permission from his patron, so Emanuel bided his time, enjoying meanwhile the stimulating mental climate of the Prussian capital, where he made friends with various prominent writers and thinkers. Influenced by the prevailing tendency for theoretical speculation, he published in 1753 his epoch-making *Essay on the True Art of Playing Keyboard Instruments*. The pedagogic interests and clear logical thinking which he had inherited from his father, combined with a superb mastery of the clavier, enabled Emanuel to produce a textbook which was to prove of paramount importance for his own time as well as for later generations.

In June 1767 an opening occurred in Hamburg which seemed too attractive for Emanuel to pass over. His godfather, the prolific Georg Philipp Telemann, had died, and Emanuel applied for the deceased master's post as musical director of Hamburg's churches. He was chosen from four distinguished applicants, and

CARL PHILIPP EMANUEL BACH (1714–1788)

by pleading ill health he succeeded, with the help of the King's sister, Princess Amalia, in getting his release from the Prussian court. Henceforth he worked in Hamburg, greatly enjoying the freedom from etiquette and again making friends with the most superior minds of the town. Financially he was quite well off; since in true Bach tradition he was thrifty and exhibited a certain business acumen in handling the sales of his own works, he was able to lead a comfortable life and to gratify his passion for collecting. To this hobby of Emanuel's we owe much of our knowledge of Bach history, for he loyally and painstakingly preserved the family chronicle laid down by Sebastian, certain family portraits, the "Alt-Bachisches Archiv," and last but not least numerous works by his father.

Apart from Sebastian himself, Emanuel and his half brother and pupil, Johann Christian, were the most influential and famous members of the family. Unlike his brother Friedemann, who was unable to reconcile the past and the present, Emanuel showed an open mind for new developments without forgetting the great achievements of the late baroque style. Thus he became one of the key figures in the transitional period between the era of Johann Sebastian and that of the Viennese classical school, and a vital link between old and new trends.

Emanuel introduced operatic recitatives, ariosos, and other forms of vocal music into his instrumental compositions and thereby increased their subjective and emotional character. His works reflect the trend towards a language of the heart advocated by the proponents of sensibility. Yet he did not follow their precepts uncritically. His mature compositions were as far removed from tearful sentimentality as they were from the shallow superficiality of the fashionable *style galant*. The Bach heritage revealed itself in the depth and vigor of his idiom. It was this peculiar mixture of subjectivity and strength which exercised so irresistible an appeal on Haydn and young Beethoven. The influence of Emanuel's music was facilitated by the wide circulation given to his compositions, the greater part of which were printed in his lifetime. Although he was particularly successful as a clavier composer, he contributed (as did his father) to all the forms of vocal and instrumental music of his time except the opera. Emanuel's output was so large that a detailed listing would by far exceed the scope of these notes. The following approximate figures might help to give an idea of its size:

about   15 organ sonatas and fugues for organ or clavier
about 200 sonatas, sonatinas, rondos, fantasias, concertos, sinfonias for clavier
about 120 smaller compositions (menuettos, polaccas, solfeggios, etc.) for clavier
about   10 sets of variations for clavier
about   50 concertos for 1 clavier and orchestra

CARL PHILIPP EMANUEL BACH (1714–1788)

about   80 clavier cadenzas to various concertos and sonatas

          2 concertos for 2 claviers and orchestra

         15 sonatinas for 1 or 2 solo claviers, string and wind instruments

about   9 concertos for a solo instrument (other than clavier) and orchestra

about   60 duos for various instrumental combinations

about   50 trios and quartets for various instrumental combinations

about   15 quintets and pieces for larger instrumental combinations

         19 symphonies

about   185 sacred songs and chorales

about   105 secular songs and arias

about   50 motets, psalms, choruses, cantatas and oratorios

As an example of Emanuel's chamber music style, we present the first and second movements from his Sonata in C major for the harpsichord with the accompaniment of violin and violoncello. This composition forms part of a set of six trios first published in 1776 by Brenner in London, and two years later by Hummel in Berlin and Amsterdam. Our edition is not based on these prints, but on the composer's original manuscript.

The trio clearly reveals the preponderance of the keyboard instrument. The cello part doubles the left hand of the clavier, while the violin usually reinforces the clavier part or plays a middle voice. Obviously the clavierist could also perform the piece alone if no strings were available. According to the custom of the time, the harpsichord part is not completely written out. The composer expected the clavierist to provide a fuller texture than the music shows, and our edition accordingly offers in smaller print some suggestions for the execution of this part.

While these two movements display a gracefully tender character, our second example, the song *Trennung* (Separation) offers a weird picture of yearning and despair. In the octaves of the bass we seem to hear bells intoning farewell, while diminished and augmented intervals create a sultry atmosphere. Not many songs of equally expressive power were produced in the eighteenth century.

A free English translation of the text reads:

> There strikes the hour of parting, cruelly to separate us two. How can I live, O maiden, without you? To every joy a stranger I live for naught but torment, and you, perhaps for ever, will forget me now, O Daphne!

The third example presented here is Emanuel's Symphony in E minor of 1756. The work seems to have made a great impression on contemporary music lovers. Hasse called it "an unequalled masterpiece," and three different versions of it

CARL PHILIPP EMANUEL BACH (1714–1788)

have survived, one for strings only, another for strings and wind instruments, a third for clavier solo. We are reproducing here the string version from a print issued in the composer's lifetime. The powerful first movement, with its unexpected rests, its alternation between unison passages and harmonized sections, and its dynamic contrasts carefully marked by the composer, gives a good idea of Emanuel's personal style. A stirring transition leads to the simple and heartfelt slow movement. The turbulent finale once more intimates a revolutionary spirit, and its bold musical language seems to point to works of the romantic era.

SOURCE OF COMPOSITIONS REPRODUCED HERE

Sonata in C: Autograph in Universitätsbibliothek, Tübingen. FP.
"Die Trennung": Friedländer, *Das deutsche Lied im 18. Jahrhundert*. Leipzig, 1902.
Sinfonia: Printed parts of 1759 (formerly owned by George B. Weston) at Harvard University, Cambridge, Massachusetts. FP.

BIBLIOGRAPHY

C. P. E. Bach, *Essay on the True Art of Playing Keyboard Instruments*, translated and edited by W. J. Mitchell. New York, 1949.
C. H. Bitter, *C. P. E. und W. F. Bach und deren Brüder*. Berlin, 1868.
A. E. Cherbuliez, *C. P. E. Bach*. Zürich, 1940.
K. Geiringer, pp. 336–377.
H. Miessner, *Philipp Emanuel Bach in Hamburg*. Leipzig, 1929.
K. F. L. Nohl, *Musikerbriefe*. Leipzig, 1873. (Emanuel's autobiography is here reproduced.)
E. Reeser, *The Sons of Bach*. Stockholm, 1949, pp. 24–43.
E. F. Schmid, *C. P. E. Bach und seine Kammermusik*. Kassel, 1931.
E. F. Schmid in *MGG*, pp. 924–942.
R. Steglich, "C. P. E. Bach und der Dresdner Kreuzkantor G. A. Homilius im Musikleben ihrer Zeit," *BJ*, 1915.
O. Vrieslander, *C. P. E. Bach*. München, 1923.

Thematic catalog compiled by A. Wotquenne. Leipzig, 1905.

CURRENT EDITIONS OF OTHER WORKS (Because of their abundance, only a limited number are listed here.)

Works for Clavier

6 Sonatas for Clavier, dedicated to the King of Prussia (Steglich). *NMA*, 1927–1928.
6 Sonatas for Clavier, dedicated to the Duke of Württemberg (Steglich). *NMA*, 1927–1928.
6 Collections of "Sonaten . . . für Kenner und Liebhaber" for Clavier (Krebs). B & H, 1895.
18 "Probestücke zum Versuch . . ." for Clavier (Doflein). Mainz: Schott, 1935.
"Sonaten und Charakterstücke" (Mies). Augsburg: Böhm, 1928.
"Kleine Stücke für Klavier" (Vrieslander). *NMA*, 1930.
(Selected) Works for Clavier (Schenker). Vienna: Universal-Edition, 1902.
4 Duets for 2 Claviers (Oberdörffer). BV, 1944.

CARL PHILIPP EMANUEL BACH (1714–1788)

Concertos

Concerto for Clavier and Orchestra in d (Schering), *DDT*, 29/30.

Concerto for Clavier and Orchestra in D (Landshoff). Berlin: Adler, 1932.

Concertos for Clavier and Orchestra in F and g (Oberdörffer). BV, 1952.

Concertos for Clavier and Orchestra in c, D, D, E flat and G, Arranged for 2 Claviers (Riemann). Leipzig: Steingräber.

Concertos for 2 Claviers and Orchestra in F and E flat (Schwartz). Leipzig: Steingräber, 1914–1918.

Concerto for Oboe and Orchestra in B flat (Lauschmann). Bad Godesberg: Forberg, 1952.

Concerto for Violoncello or Flute or Harpsichord and Orchestra in a (Altmann). Leipzig: Eulenburg, 1938.

Concerto for Violoncello and Orchestra in B flat (Klengel). B & H, 1931.

Chamber Music and Symphonies

Duos for Flute and Violin (Stephan). *NMA*, 1929.

Fantasia (Sonata) for Clavier and Violin (Schering). Leipzig: Kahnt, 1938.

Sonata for Clavier and Violin in D (Schmid). Karlsbad: Hohler, 1932.

Sonata for Clavier and Flute in C (Leeuwen). Leipzig: Zimmermann, 1923.

12 Two- and Three-Part Pieces for Flute or Violin and Clavier (Hirsch). Berlin: Breslauer, 1928.

Trio Sonata for 2 Violins and Clavier in G (Riemann). B & H, 1904.

Trio Sonata for Flute, Violin and Continuo in B flat (Landshoff). Leipzig: Peters, 1936.

Trio Sonata for Flute, Violin and Continuo in b (Ermeler). Leipzig: Zimmermann, 1932.

Trio Sonata for 2 Flutes and Clavier in E (Walther). Leipzig: Zimmermann, 1935.

Quartets for Flute, Viola, Cello and Clavier in C, D, and G (Schmid). BV, 1952.

6 Marches for 2 Oboes, 2 Clarinets, 2 Horns, Bassoon and Percussion (Simon). New York: Marks, 1948.

4 Orchestral Symphonies (Steglich). *RD*, vol. 18.

3 Symphonies for Strings (Schmid). *NMA*, 1931–1937.

Vocal Works

25 "Ausgewählte geistliche Gesänge" for Voice and Clavier (Dittberner). Leipzig: Kahnt, 1918.

30 "Geistliche Lieder" for Voice and Clavier (Roth). Leipzig: Peters, 1922.

"Lieder und Gesänge" for Voice and Clavier (Vrieslander). München: Musikalische Stunden-bücher, 1922.

"Phillis und Tirsis," solo cantata (Walther). B & H, 1928.

"Heilig" for Double Chorus and Orchestra (Geiringer). St. Louis: Concordia, 1955.

"Magnificat" (Deis). New York: Schirmer, 1950.

"Die Israeliten in der Wüste" (Schletterer). Wolfenbüttel: Holler, 1864.

"Auferstehung und Himmelfahrt" (Schletterer). Wolfenbüttel: Holler, 1865.

Versuch über die wahre Art das Clavier zu spielen (Niemann). Leipzig: Kahnt, 1906. (See Bibliography for English translation.)

Carl Philipp Emanuel Bach (1714–1788)

Andantino grazioso and Larghetto

From Sonata in C for Harpsichord,
Violin, and Violoncello

II.

Larghetto

Carl Philipp Emanuel Bach (1714–1788)

Die Trennung   For Voice and Clavier

Sehr langsam und traurig

Da schlägt des Ab - schieds stun - - de, um

grau - sam uns zu tren - nen! Wie werd' ich le - - ben kön - nen,

Mäd - - chen oh - - ne dich?_____ Ein Fremd - - ling al - - ler

Freu - den, leb ich nur, um zu lei - - den, und

du viel - leicht auf e - - wig ver - giest_____ nun, Daph - - ne, mich!

Carl Philipp Emanuel Bach (1714–1788)

Sinfonia

For Strings and Continuo

141

142

143

146

2. Andante moderato

151

3. Allegro

155

Johann Ernst Bach (1722–1777)

JOHANN ERNST, a son of Johann Bernhard, may be counted among Sebastian Bach's most successful pupils. Being a godson of the Thomas Cantor, he was sent for his final musical training to Leipzig and there received decisive stimulation from his great kinsman. After a short stay at the Thomas school, which he had to leave because of an unauthorized absence (a misdemeanor for which many Bachs seem to have had a penchant), he remained in Leipzig to work with his godfather. Later he entered the university to study law, but at the age of nineteen he had to return to Eisenach to act as a substitute for his ailing father. When J. Bernhard died in 1749, Ernst succeeded him to the post of organist, and at the same time he tried to make use of his legal training as a barrister. Attempts to improve his standing in this field failed, and all extra-musical activities came to an end in 1756 when the new ruler of the principality of Weimar appointed Ernst Bach his Court Conductor. The composer moved to Weimar, where he admirably carried out his new duties, organizing a good group of players despite a small budget and providing significant compositions of his own for the performances at court. Unfortunately this fruitful phase was abruptly terminated in 1758 when the young Prince suddenly died. His widow dismissed the orchestra, and although she allowed the conductor to retain his title and allotted him a pension for life, Ernst saw no reason to stay on at Weimar. He returned to Eisenach, where during his absence a substitute had served as organist and resumed his old duties. A few years later he also accepted a position as *Kastenverwalter* (bookkeeper) for his church. He raised a large family and trained his eldest son, Johann Georg, to succeed him in both his occupations. Georg eventually rose to higher social rank, being ultimately appointed chamberlain of the Eisenach Council. With Georg's death the line of Bach organists in Eisenach came to an end, after having served in the Georgenkirche from 1665 to 1797.

The number of compositions by J. Ernst known today is small. They include a few works for organ and clavier solo, six sonatas for violin and a keyboard instrument, eighteen fables for voice and clavier, a motet-like "short mass" (Kyrie and Gloria), the "Passion Oratorio," and about ten secular or sacred cantatas. Even this limited output is sufficient to reveal an interesting creative

JOHANN ERNST BACH (1722–1777)

personality who helped shape musical trends in the transitional phase between the baroque and classical eras. As a youth Ernst was strongly influenced by the art of his teacher and godfather. Later he espoused in his instrumental works the tenets of the graceful and lighthearted *style galant,* while his vocal works followed instead the more sentimental and subjective idiom of Karl Heinrich Graun and other North German composers of sacred music.

The "Largo" and "Allegro" for violin and clavier in our anthology are the middle and final movements of the second sonata in a set published in 1770 by Griesbach of Eisenach. The success of these three sonatas with the public is proved by the fact that the composer was able to present three new works of the kind in 1772 and to have his first set reprinted in 1780. Our specimen reveals Ernst's tendency to allot tasks of equal importance to both the stringed and the keyboard instruments. The violinist is no longer considered a mere accompanist, and it is characteristic that the title page of the old print omits the traditional reference to the subordinate role of the string instrument. In the heartfelt "Largo" the right hand of the clavier and the part of the violin are artfully interwoven, while the sparkling "Allegro" shows the two instruments engaged in a lively conversation to which each partner significantly contributes.

As an example of Ernst's vocal style we present two choruses, separated by a tenor solo, from his extensive setting of Psalm VI ("O Lord, rebuke me not in Thine anger"). In the choral sections the accompanying string group is mainly used to underline the passionate urgency expressed by the voice parts. In the solo number, however, the instruments greatly contribute to the description of fear and confusion filling the soul that "is sore vexed." It is a work worthy of the great tradition established in Ernst's branch of the Bach family.

The text of the excerpt reproduced here reads according to the King James version:

> Have mercy upon me, O Lord; for I am weak: O Lord, heal me; for my bones are vexed.
> My soul is also sore vexed: but thou, O Lord, how long?

SOURCE OF COMPOSITIONS REPRODUCED HERE

Largo and Allegro: 3 Sonaten für das Klavier und 1 Violine. Eisenach: Griesbach's Söhne, 1770; Library of Congress, Washington, D. C. FP.
Psalm VI: MS formerly owned by George B. Weston, now at Harvard University, Cambridge, Massachusetts. FP.

BIBLIOGRAPHY

K. Geiringer, pp. 451–463.

JOHANN ERNST BACH (1722–1777)

G. Kraft in *MGG*, pp. 960–962.

H. Kretzschmar, Preface to *DDT*, vol. 42.

H. Kühn, "4 Organisten Eisenachs aus bachischem Geschlecht" in *Bach in Thüringen*. Berlin, 1950.

H. Löffler, "Bache bei Sebastian Bach" in *BJ*, 1949–1950.

CURRENT EDITIONS OF OTHER WORKS

Fantasy and Fugue in F for Clavier (Pauer) in *Alte Meister des Klavierspiels*. B & H.

Sonata for Clavier and Violin in D (Küster). *NMA*, 1927.

"Sammlung auserlesener Fabeln" (Kretzschmar), *DDT*, vol. 42.

"Passions-Oratorium" (Kromolicki), *DDT*, vol. 48.

Johann Ernst Bach (1722–1777)

Largo and Allegro

From Sonata in F for Clavier and Violin

160

Johann Ernst Bach (1722–1777)

Three Movements

167

169

171

173

Johann Christoph Friedrich Bach (1732–1795)

JOHANN CHRISTOPH FRIEDRICH, the second surviving son from Sebastian's union with Anna Magdalena Wilcken, revealed decided musical gifts although he lacked the qualities of artistic leadership exhibited by his half brother Emanuel. His life developed in accordance with traditions established by the older members of the family. At the age of nineteen he was offered a position at the ducal court of Schaumburg-Lippe in Bückeburg. In consequence he gave up his law studies at Leipzig University to become chamber musician in the small Westphalian town, and there he stayed for forty-six years until his death, serving three successive rulers. In 1759 he rose to the rank of concertmaster and conductor, a position formerly held by an Italian maestro, and henceforth he devoted much energy to the organization and training of his orchestra so that it was eventually counted among the best in Germany.

The musical life at the small court was quite active. Important contemporary works were performed under the direction of the "Bückeburg Bach," who also continuously provided compositions of his own whenever an occasion called for them. Friedrich followed the example of his father by marrying young; his wife was a court singer as his mother had been, and the couple raised nine children, of whom the eldest son seemed destined to carry on the traditions of the Bach musicians. The monotony of service at Bückeburg was broken once when Friedrich traveled with this son to London to stay with his brilliant and glamorous brother Christian, and the visit afforded him much artistic stimulation. It was the only contact Friedrich ever made with the big world. He seems not to have minded the narrowly restricted existence at Bückeburg, and he put up with a modest salary. For him life at the little court had the great advantage of giving him the opportunity to devote all his energies to his beloved art. Contemporaries praise his outstanding pianistic performances; Friedemann Bach even went so far as to say that among the brothers Friedrich was "the strongest on the clavier." Yet he did not attempt to win laurels as a virtuoso but found his greatest joy in creative work, which he carried on to the very last days of his life.

He seems to have been almost as prolific and hard-working as his half brother Emanuel, with whom he was on excellent terms. Although a substantial number

JOHANN CHRISTOPH FRIEDRICH BACH (1732–1795)

of his works appear to be lost, there is still a great amount of material available that gives a clear idea of Friedrich's creative gifts. Among the works preserved we find the following:

       11 sonatas and 1 sonatina for clavier, as well as numerous smaller pieces
        2 sonatas for clavier 4 hands
about 15 duos or trios for various combinations such as cello and clavier; flute and clavier; flute, violin, clavier; violin, viola, clavier
        6 string quartets
        6 flute quartets
        1 sextet
        1 septet
        6 clavier concertos
       14 symphonies
       55 sacred and numerous secular songs
        5 monodramas (solo cantatas)
        2 motets
        3 cantatas
        3 oratorios ("Der Tod Jesu," "Die Kindheit Jesu," "Die Auferweckung Lazarus")

The works he wrote in his thirties and forties clearly reveal the influence of Italian music then dominant at the court at Bückeburg. This was the kind of music his patron expected from him. At the same time Friedrich also felt attracted by the work of Emanuel Bach and other North German composers. During the later part of his life he subtly changed his style, largely because of the work of his younger brother Christian. Subjective and passionate features receded into the background, and the composer aimed to create an atmosphere of gaiety, tenderness, and warmth. Friedrich, who was born in the same year as Joseph Haydn, assumed in his last concertos and symphonies a style somewhat resembling that of his great contemporary.

Our anthology presents a minuet for clavier taken from the collection *Musikalische Nebenstunden* (Music for Leisure Hours), printed in 1787. This was a quarterly publication of various compositions by Friedrich, such as works for clavier alone, violin sonatas, and songs. The composer intended, as he states in the preface, "to offer to both the more experienced player and the beginner music likely to entertain." While there seems to have been at first lively interest in the venture, Friedrich was unable to continue it after the first four issues had been published. Our minuet was clearly meant to be educational; it is a light and unassuming piece free of technical difficulties.

In his vocal output Friedrich showed a predilection for the solo cantata, which he liked to designate as "monodrama." The earliest of these works and the only one using an Italian text is "Cassandra," for contralto, strings, and cembalo. This work — until quite recently considered lost — seems to have been written around 1771; J. G. Herder, the great German writer, mentioned its performance after his arrival in Bückeburg in that year. The text reflects the ardor and passion of the "Storm and Stress" movement, which was reaching its climax at that time. Friedrich's music does not quite follow the lead of the libretto. The aria included in our anthology, in which Cassandra addresses Andromache, is imbued with warm tenderness as though the composer wanted to describe the compassion which the prophetess of evil tidings felt for the terrible fate of her brother and his wife. The choice of instruments is remarkable. While the composer is satisfied to use a figured bass in the recitative, he adds in the following aria a violino obbligato as well as a solo cello, and he partially elaborates the cembalo part. (In our selection Friedrich's own notes are reproduced in larger type than those inserted by the editor.) Thus a clavier trio is used to accompany the voice, a most attractive device of the kind later adopted by Haydn and others for their arrangements of Scottish and Irish songs.

A free English translation of the Italian text reads:

> Recitative: Andromache, you are silent? And are you crouched at the bottom of the great house weaving bright linens? Come out and see your husband before he closes his eyes.
> Aria: Come, O spouse, fortunate are you if permitted to catch the last breath which leaves his beloved face as he joins the shadows. In the repose of Elysium sojourning under a myrtle he will await you with the heroes.

While "Cassandra" remained in manuscript, our third example is based on parts printed in the composer's lifetime. Around the year 1768 M. C. Bock in Hamburg issued Friedrich's six quartets for transverse flute, violin, viola, and figured bass with a dedication to the composer's patron, Count Wilhelm of Schaumburg-Lippe. They were printed in 1925 in an arrangement for flute and clavier, but so far none of these delightful chamber music compositions have been available in their original form. Like the other pieces of the set, our Quartet in C major is in two movements only, the first a graceful allegretto, the second a merry scherzo. The work displays the true spirit of chamber music, allotting equal shares to each of the three upper voices and at times even freeing the bass from its monotonous role as mere support.

JOHANN CHRISTOPH FRIEDRICH BACH (1732–1795)

SOURCE OF COMPOSITIONS REPRODUCED HERE

Menuet: "Musikalische Nebenstunden. Vier Theile," Bibliothèque du Conservatoire, Brussels. FP.

"Cassandra": MS in Bibliothèque du Conservatoire, Brussels. FP.

Quartet in C: "Sei quartetti a flauto traverso, violino, viola e basso." Bibliothèque du Conservatoire, Brussels. FP.

BIBLIOGRAPHY

R. Benecke in *MGG*, pp. 956–960.

K. Geiringer, pp. 378–403.

G. Hey, "Zur Biographie J. Friedrich Bachs und seiner Familie," *BJ*, 1933.

R. Reeser, *The Sons of Bach*. Stockholm, 1949, pp. 44–53.

G. Schünemann, "Johann Christoph Friedrich Bach," *BJ*, 1914.

C. U. von Ulmenstein, "Die Nachkommen des Bückeburger Bach," *Archiv für Musikforschung*, 1939.

Thematic catalog compiled by Georg Schünemann in *DDT*, vol. 56.

CURRENT EDITIONS OF OTHER WORKS

Instrumental Works

Sonatas in A, D, and A for Clavier Solo and Sonata in C for Clavier four hands (Schünemann). Leipzig: Siegel, 1920.

Allegretto con 18 variazioni f. clavier (Riemann). Leipzig: Steingräber.

Rondo in C for Clavier (Pauer) in *Alte Klaviermusik*, vol. 4. B & H.

Sonata in A for Clavier Duet (Riemann). Leipzig: Steingräber.

Sonata in A for Violoncello and Clavier (Smith). Braunschweig: Litolff, 1905.

6 Sonatas for Flute and Clavier arranged from Flute Quartets (Schwedler & Wittenbecher). Leipzig: Zimmermann.

Sonata a cembalo concertato, flauto e violino (Hinnenthal). B & H, 1937.

Trio for Violin, Viola, Clavier in G; Trio for Flute, Violin, Clavier in C; Septet for 2 Horns, Oboe, Violin, Viola, Cello, Clavier in C (Schünemann). Leipzig: Siegel, 1920.

6 Quartets for 2 Violins, Viola, Cello (Duttenhofer). Paris: Senart, 1922.

Vocal Works

"Die Amerikanerin" (Walter). B & H, 1919.

Motets: "Ich lieg und schlafe," "Wachet auf" (Schünemann). Leipzig: Siegel, 1921.

"Die Kindheit Jesu" and "Die Auferweckung Lazarus" (Schünemann), *DDT*, vol. 56.

Johann Christoph Friedrich Bach (1732–1795)

Menuet

For Clavier

Trio

Menuet D.C.

Johann Christoph Friedrich Bach (1732–1795)

Recitativo and Aria

From the Solo Cantata *Cassandra*

182

Vie - ni o spo - sa te____ fe - li - ce se____ ti li - ce

(Fine)

184

di __ rac - cor l'e - stre - mo spir - to che ab - ban - do - na il

ca - ro ____ vi - so e con _____ l'om - bra se - ne và;

che ab - ban - do __ na il dol - ce vi - so, e __ con l'om - bra

se — ne và; e con l'om - bra se — ne và.

se ne và, vie — ni o spo-sa se ti li-ce di___ rac-cor l'e—

stre — mo spir-to che ab-ban-do-na il dol — ce vi-so

188

e —— con l'om - bra se ne và e con l'om - bra se ne

và.

(Fine)

Nel ri - po - so del-l'E - li - so sog - gior -

nan - do sot - to un mir - to co - gli E - roi t'at - ten - de -

rà t'at - ten - de - rà, nel ri -

po - so del — l'E - li - so sog - gior - nan - do

sot - to un — mir - to cog - li — E - roi t'at - ten - de -

rà, t'at - ten — — — — — — — — — — — de - rà.

Da Capo

191

Johann Christoph Friedrich Bach (1732–1795)

Sonata in C

For Flute, Violin, Viola, and Continuo

194

Scherzo

Poco Allegro

201

Johann Christian Bach (1735–1782)

JOHANN CHRISTIAN, Sebastian's youngest son, led a life strangely divergent from that of his kinspeople. His elder brother Friedrich had exemplified the virtues typical of the older Bachs; keeping the same rather obscure position throughout his life, marrying in young years, raising a large family, and, most of all, being firmly rooted in the Lutheran faith. Christian, however, traveled quite a different path. He exchanged sedentary habits for sojourns in foreign countries, obscurity for the limelight of the theater, Protestantism for Catholicism. At the age of fifteen he lost his father, and thus the impact of Sebastian's personality was felt less by Christian than by any of the other sons. After the Thomas Cantor's death, Emanuel took the youth into his home in Berlin, and under the guidance of that eminent teacher Christian developed into a brilliant clavier virtuoso and a highly promising composer.

His interest was centered on a type of music neglected by his relatives. Opera fascinated him, and in order to study it in its homeland, Christian at the age of twenty contrived to travel to Italy. There the gifted, handsome musician quickly established important contacts with a wealthy count who was willing to support him, as well as with the foremost Italian music scholar, Padre Martini, whose instruction greatly added to Christian's musical knowledge. Sojourns at Naples also increased his familiarity with opera. Thanks to the Count's influence Christian, who had been converted to the Roman Catholic faith, was appointed organist to the cathedral of Milan. At the same time he received commissions for operas and won great applause with dramatic works at both Turin and Naples. His fame traveled to England, where Italian opera was enjoying a great vogue, and in 1762 he was invited to the King's Theatre in the British capital. Here again he was very successful with two new operas he offered, and although his connection with the King's Theatre was severed after one season, he decided to stay in London and accept the appointment as music master to the Queen. He led there an extremely active life, writing operas as well as numerous other works, conducting jointly with C. Friedrich Abel a series of important subscription concerts, and giving music instruction to the nobility. In his teaching he was assisted after 1773 by his wife, the Italian singer Cecilia Grassi, whom he married when he was thirty-eight.

JOHANN CHRISTIAN BACH (1735–1782)

Occasionally Christian visited the continent of Europe, as he was commissioned twice to write an opera for the German Elector at Mannheim and once to compose a dramatic work for Paris. In spite of such glittering success and a good income, Christian was unable to accumulate any reasonable savings. He led a luxurious life, was generous to his friends, and in 1773 spent large amounts on an ambitious remodeling of the concert hall needed for his subscription series. Unfortunately the London public, with its notorious hunger for novelties, was growing less interested in the Bach-Abel concerts, and thus Christian found it difficult to pay back the sums loaned to him. His financial worries were further increased through the meteoric rise to popularity of the German music teacher Johann Samuel Schroeter, and all these problems, combined with the effects of incessant creative work and a life exposed to the intrigues of the operatic world, undermined his health. Throughout the summer of 1781 he was ailing, and on New Year's Day in 1782 he died, before he had reached the age of forty-seven.

As an artist Christian showed the drive and energy of his father. In his short life he produced a surprisingly large number of works, which included two types of composition shunned by other Bachs: opera and Catholic church music. As a matter of fact the thematic catalog of his works comprises practically every kind of music cultivated in his time. The following list gives an idea of his output:

fuga on BACH for pianoforte or organ
about 35 sonatas and smaller pieces for harpsichord or pianoforte
about 12 duos for two players on 1 or 2 claviers
about 120 duos, trios, quartets, and quintets for different instrumental combinations
about 35 concertos for harpsichord or pianoforte with orchestra
about 90 symphonies, overtures, concerted symphonies, and other works for orchestra
about 70 pieces of church music
about 90 English and Italian songs, duets, arias, cantatas
one oratorio
11 operas and contributions to several pasticcios

Christian's powerful mental curiosity drove him to become thoroughly acquainted with various musical idioms. In younger years he was impressed by the style of his father and more still by that of his half brother Emanuel. Later the brilliance and sensuousness of Italian opera and the melodic grandeur of Italian church music exercised noticeable influences on him. As a result he developed a light, dreamy, and often sparkling tonal language that was yet based on solid knowledge and craftsmanship. Young Mozart was deeply impressed by the lovely cantilenas in Christian's music, its sensitive elegance, and its effective use of melodic contrasts. The Salzburg composer, who was a cosmopolitan himself and gained inspiration from the works of men professing the most variegated artistic creeds, saluted a kindred spirit in Sebastian's youngest son. He greatly liked him as a person and he adopted in his own music features of Christian's peculiar blend of various stylistic elements. Christian more than any other Bach came close to the classical style in music. It was a tragedy that his life was cut short at a time when musical classicism was moving towards its zenith.

As an example of Christian's ability to adapt the style of the Italian opera to the specific requirements of English popular music, we include a song printed in 1767 which the composer wrote for the concerts at Vauxhall. This popular place of entertainment, where open-air music was regularly offered, may have appealed to him as it appealed to Joseph Haydn in 1792. The Austrian composer made detailed notes in his diary on the impressions he received there and stated that "the place and its diversions had no equal in the world." Even to his critical ears the music produced there sounded "fairly good." In Christian's time Vauxhall possessed a great attraction in the gifted singer Mrs. Weichsell, for whom our song was destined. It is a typical rococo piece both in the text and the music, which offered a well-trained soprano ample opportunity to display grace and technical skill.

Our second example presents three of the attractive instrumental numbers Christian wrote for his opera "Amadis des Gaules," performed in 1779 in Paris. This work, the composer's only contribution to French opera, is based on a text adapted from a libretto used by J. B. Lully almost a hundred years earlier. Following the prevailing tendency in French opera, the score contains numerous ballet scenes. The solemn "Lentement" and the pair of graceful gavottes are inserted near the end of the first act. They display both the economy and the skill with which the great symphonic composer handled the resources of the orchestra. The "Tambourin" which forms the end of the second act represents a type of dance popular in eighteenth-century French opera. Originally the term *tambourin* was used for a Provençal drum played together with the *galoubet,* a shrill small flute; subsequently compositions imitating the music produced by these instruments were given the same name, and this form of *tambourin* is to be found in earlier French operas. A ritornel employing piccolo flute and timpani returns four times in Christian's rondo-like composition, giving a gay and saucy character to the brilliant number. The noted author Baron von Grimm may have had such pieces in mind when he remarked in his *Correspondance*: "M. Bach's style exhales pure and sustained harmony; his instrumentation is rich and delicate."

SOURCE OF COMPOSITIONS REPRODUCED HERE

"Lovely Yet Ungrateful Swain": No. 4 in *A Second Collection of Favourite Songs sung at Vaux Hall by Mrs. Pinto and Mrs. Weichsell* . . . , London: Welcker, 1767; copy formerly the property of George B. Weston, now of Harvard University, Cambridge, Massachusetts. FP.

"Amadis des Gaules: Tragédie lirique de Quinault": Paris, 1780; copy at Library of Congress, Washington, D. C. FP.

BIBLIOGRAPHY

H. Abert, "J. Ch. Bach's italienische Opern und ihr Einfluss auf Mozart," *Zeitschrift f. Musikwissenschaft*, 1919.

K. Geiringer, pp. 404–444.

R. Reeser, *The Sons of Bach*. Stockholm [1949]. Pp. 53–63.

G. de Saint-Foix, "A propos de J. Ch. Bach," *Revue de Musicologie*, 1926.

H. P. Schökel, *J. Ch. Bach und die Instrumentalmusik seiner Zeit*. Wolfenbüttel, 1926.

M. Schwartz, *J. Ch. Bach. Sein Leben und sein Werk*. Leipzig, 1901.

C. S. Terry, *John Christian Bach*. London, 1929.

F. Tutenberg, *Die Sinfonik J. Ch. Bachs*. Wolfenbüttel, 1928.

A. L. Wenk, *Beiträge zur Kenntnis des Opernschaffens von J. Ch. Bach*. (Unpublished dissertation). 1932.

H. Wirth in *MGG*, pp. 942–954.

Thematic catalog compiled by C. S. Terry (see above), pp. 192–361.

CURRENT EDITIONS OF OTHER WORKS (Because of their abundance, only a limited number are listed here.)

Works for Clavier

10 Clavier Sonatas (Landshoff). Leipzig: Peters, 1925.
Sonata in C for piano, four hands (Küster). *NMA*, 1927.
Sonata in F for piano, four hands (Neubauer). Münster: Bisping, 1931.
Sonata in G for 2 pianos (Hudnik). Mainz: Schott, 1935.

Chamber Music

Sonatas in B flat, C, G, A, F, op. 10, nos. 1–5, for Piano and Violin (Landshoff). London: Hinrichsen.
Sonatas in D, G, A, op. 16, nos. 1, 2, 4, for Piano and Violin (Küster). *NMA*, 1927–1933.
6 Duets for 2 Violins (Friedrich). *NMA*, 1936.
3 String Trios (Upmeyer). BV, 1948.
6 Nocturnes for 2 Violins and Viola (Beck). New York Public Library, 1937.
Trio in D for Piano, Violin and Cello (Riemann). B & H, 1903.
3 Flute Quartets, op. 8 (Küster and Glöde). BV, 1927.

JOHANN CHRISTIAN BACH (1735–1782)

6 Quintets (Steglich), *RD*, Abteilung "Kammermusik," vol. I.

Concertos and Symphonies

Concertos in B flat and D for Piano and Orchestra (Landshoff). Leipzig: Peters, 1931–1932.
Concerto in E flat for Clavier and Orchestra (Praetorius). Leipzig: Eulenburg, 1937.
Concerto in A for Clavier and Orchestra (Stadlmann). Mainz: Schott, 1935.
Sinfonia concertante in E flat (Stein). Leipzig: Eulenburg, 1935.
Sinfonia concertante in A (Einstein). Leipzig: Eulenburg, 1934.
Symphony in D, op. 18, no. 1 (Landshoff). Leipzig: Peters, 1934.
Symphonies in E flat (op. 9, no. 2) B flat (op. 18, no. 2), D (op. 18, no. 4) (Stein). Leipzig: Peters.
Symphonies for Double Orchestra in E flat and D (Stein). Leipzig: Peters.
Symphony in G (Sondheimer). London: Bernoulli.

Vocal Works

12 Concert and Opera Arias (Landshoff). Leipzig: Peters, 1930.
2 Secular Arias (Walter). B & H, 1928.

Johann Christian Bach (1735–1782)

Lovely Yet Ungrateful Swain

For Soprano and Orchestra

All_____ your Oaths_____ and all_____ your Sighs_____

once_____ I fool___ish___ly_____ be - liev'd,_____ but_____ Pas - to - ra's

Johann Christian Bach (1735–1782)

Three Instrumental Pieces

From the Opera *Amadis des Gaules*

Lentement

*) The double bars frequently occurring in this score are presumably to be interpreted as repeat-signs.

214

Première Gavotte

216

Seconde Gavotte

Solo

(f) ... (p)

Dal segno :S:
(1re Gavotte)

cresc.

218

*) In the original edition this and the corresponding repeats are written out.

(Da capo al Fine e
poi il Minore *)

Minore

222

(Da capo al Fine
e poi il Maggiore)

223

(Da capo al Fine
e poi la Coda)

225

(Coda)

226

Wilhelm Friedrich Ernst Bach (1759–1845)

WILHELM was the last professional musician among Sebastian's descendants. In him we see the splendid drive of former Bach artists dwindle, and the decline in the family talent is undeniable. Wilhelm received instruction in piano and composition from his father, the "Bückeburg Bach," and when he had gained a high standard of proficiency, he went to London to complete his training with his uncle Christian. He became a fine virtuoso and teacher, and possibly would have won a good position in London had not the untimely death of his brilliant uncle uprooted his life there. Christian's home was broken up; debtors claimed all that was left of the property, and the widow returned to Italy. Thus there was no foothold for Wilhelm in London and he turned homeward, making concert appearances in France and Holland. Subsequently he settled down as music director at Minden, a Westphalian town not far from Bückeburg.

Political events seemed to carry the young musician towards success. The new occupant of the Prussian throne, Friedrich Wilhelm II, who was a genuine friend of music, visited Minden. Wilhelm offered a cantata of his own to welcome the King, and impressed him as favorably as young Emanuel had impressed his predecessor. So the monarch engaged Wilhelm Bach for Berlin, appointing him music master to the Queen. This was a stroke of luck, for at the Prussian court music was earnestly cultivated, and an ambitious and gifted musician had splendid opportunities there. Wilhelm lacked ambition, however, especially when he was deprived of the moral support lent by his father and his uncle. He shunned the limelight and we hear nothing of appearances at court as a piano virtuoso. He was content to teach the Queen and the royal Princes, and when his royal mistress died in 1810, he retired from court work, having received a pension from one of the Princes. Thus he led a quiet, uneventful life — which may have contributed to his reaching the ripe age of eighty-six. Although he composed a good deal, few of his works obtained a wide circulation, and it is significant that a Bach enthusiast like Felix Mendelssohn, who spent many years in Berlin, knew nothing of the existence of Sebastian's grandson. Only when the Bach monument was unveiled in Leipzig in 1843 did the musical world become aware of the "worthy head, bear-

WILHELM FRIEDRICH ERNST BACH (1759–1845)

ing so sacred a name," as Robert Schumann expressed it. Wilhelm was "the celebrated hero of the day, a very old man, yet vigorous, with snow-white hair and expressive features."

In order to get an idea of Wilhelm Bach's artistic personality, we have to consider the musical world at the time of his birth rather than during the full extent of his long life, which exceeded that of any other Bach composer. Wilhelm's formative years were spent in London with his uncle, and he never forgot the artistic impressions he received there. Although Beethoven, Schubert, Schumann, and Chopin wrote their works in his lifetime, he remained faithful to the ideal of a style full of light grace and charm which he had cultivated at the age of twenty. The brittle elegance of late rococo and early classicistic music remained his goal; and of his numerous works preserved — pieces for piano solo, piano duet, and piano tercet, various works of chamber music, piano concertos, orchestral suites, symphonies, German and French songs, choruses, secular and sacred cantatas, and a "Ballet-Pantomime" — practically none show the impact of romanticism, which exercised so overwhelming an influence on the great minds of his time.

Wilhelm's sense of humor may be detected in the charming "Dreyblatt" (trefoil) for six hands on one piano, incorporated into our anthology. The composer prescribes here that the piece should be performed by a gentleman who is flanked on either side by a lady; he has to stretch his arms so as to play with the left hand the lowest and with the right hand the highest notes of the composition. The little piece with its excursion into the realm of Hungarian music is artistically quite attractive.

A similar character is revealed in Wilhelm's short cradle song reproduced here. The text, in which a mother addresses her baby son, exhibits an amusing mixture of fondness and exasperation. Musically it shows the very simple character of the strophic song before Schubert.

A free English translation of the text reads:

> Rest you gently, little laddie, you will never fare so well; in the cradle and the grave one knows nothing of sadness. You know naught of grief or worry lying in your little bed. Every morning you have your gruel which makes you more than rich.
>
> But for whole days at a time you are truly a tormentor. You whine unhappy laments, though you know nothing of pain. But that is because you are a boy. Men are, as we know, from the cradle to the grave, here for our great torment.

As a third example of the composer's style we are presenting his Sextet in E flat major for clarinet, 2 horns, violin, viola, and cello. The work, which bears no author's name, is preserved in Wilhelm's handwriting in a volume of his music purchased by the British Museum. Since the composer did offer chamber music of a similar type, we are justified in ascribing the sextet to him. It displays attractive ideas and solid craftsmanship, showing that the Bach talent was apparently still alive, if diminished, in Sebastian's grandson.

SOURCE OF COMPOSITIONS REPRODUCED HERE

"Dreyblatt": MS, British Museum, Add. 32045. FP.
"Wiegenlied einer Mutter": *Auswahl deutscher und französischer Lieder und Arietten mit Begleitung des Pianoforte*, Berlin: Hummel; Brussels, Bibliothèque du Conservatoire, E 11.598. FP.
Sextet in E flat: Score transcribed by Edward J. Dent from autograph parts in the British Museum, Add. 32043; property of George B. Weston, Cambridge, Massachusetts. FP.

BIBLIOGRAPHY

K. Geiringer, pp. 474–480.
C. S. Terry in *Grove*, pp. 328–329.

CURRENT EDITION OF OTHER WORK

Trio in G for 2 Transverse Flutes and Viola (Ermeler), BV.

Wilhelm Friedrich Ernst Bach (1759–1845)

Das Dreyblatt

For Pianoforte, six hands

N.B. Der Herr, welcher die Mittelstimme spielt, sezt sich etwas mehr zurück, als die beyden ihm zu Seyten sizenden Damen, deren Arme über den Seinigen müssen gehalten werden, so wie der enge Raum für 3 Personen etwas Zusammenschränkung erfordert.

(N.B. The gentleman playing the middle part sits slightly behind the two ladies on either side. They have to hold their arms above his, and the restricted space makes it necessary for the 3 persons to sit somewhat closely together.)

234

235

236

Wilhelm Friedrich Ernst Bach (1759–1845)

Wiegenlied einer Mutter

For Voice and Piano

Ru - he sanft du lie - ber Kna - be!
Doch bist du zu gan - zen Ta - gen

Jetzt ist dei - ne be - ste Zeit; in der Wieg' und in dem Gra - be
oft ein wah - rer Pla - ge - geist, win - selst un - zu - fried' - ne Kla - gen

weiss man nichts von Trau - rig - keit. Du kennst we - der Gram noch Sor - gen,
wenn du nichts von Schmer - zen weisst. Da - für bist du auch ein Kna - be—

ruh'st in dei - nem Bett - chen weich; Nah - rung wird dir al - le Mor - gen,
Män - ner sind, man weiss es ja, von der Wie - ge bis zum Gra - be

und das macht dich mehr als reich.
uns zur gros - sen Pla - ge da.

Wilhelm Friedrich Ernst Bach (1759–1845)

Sextet in E flat

For Clarinet, 2 Horns, Violin,
Viola, and Violoncello

240

243

Rondo, Allegretto